PRAISE FOR *MO*

"Kingsley takes us on a truly American journey of a woman who searches for compassion and meaning as she liberates herself from a loveless marriage and establishes an independent life for herself. Her struggles with the burdens of personal and family history are our struggles, and we root for her as she learns to spread her wings and fly."

Howard C. Rubin, MD
San Francisco, California

"A compelling, sometimes tearful story of a woman's struggle to survive a sexless, loveless marriage. This novel takes a hard look at Myrna's decisions and choices, which she was forced to make ... no matter what was in her heart!"

Barbara Bixon
President, AR Alan Productions
Boynton Beach, Florida

"*Mother in Name Only* is a page-turner that intersects all the heartbreaking emotions of a young mother forced by her husband to put her baby up for adoption, a taboo subject that needs to be brought to the light for healing. The arc of the protagonist Myrna Kaye is a roadmap to redemption we can all relate to, as she finds the courage to forgive herself, release resentment, and find serenity in self-acceptance. We root for Myrna because we can all relate to her struggles as a woman—and we want her to find happiness."

Leigh Rudd
CEO, IM International Publishing, Author, Screenwriter
Laguna Woods, California

"Heartbreaking intergenerational drama meets spiritual healing in *Mother in Name Only*, Diana Kingsley's debut novel about a woman married to one man while carrying the child of another and how she resolves the gutwrenching aftermath. Told with unflinching reality, this tale deftly weaves back and forth in time, whisking us on one woman's circuitous journey to reinvent herself, discovering along the way what it really means to be a mother."

Joan Liman, MD, MPH
COO, Yiddishkayt Initiative, Writer, Lyricist
New Jersey and Boca Raton, Florida

"*Mother in Name Only* is the harrowing story of a woman whose choices in life led her through the rabbit's hole, a tunnel filled with self-loathing, doubts, regrets and heart-wrenching decisions. In a style that grabs the reader from the very beginning, the protagonist navigates her past delving fiercely and fearlessly into the emotional chaos that punctuated most of her adult life. Few characters tackle the truth so head-on, and so bravely. This book will force you to take a hard look at motherhood, what it means in the bigger picture, and really examine the reasons behind the actions that sometimes we are forced to take. In the end, you will embrace the light that comes after fighting the demons in the depths of despair. A story of regrets, hope, and ultimate redemption you will never forget."

Alexandra Goodwin
Author of *Exchange at the Border*
Coral Springs, Florida

"*Mother in Name Only* is a story painfully told about a woman survivor of intense struggles, common to every woman. Kingsley's storytelling shocks, inspires, and brings tears of recognition to our eyes. This book is difficult to put down. Protagonist Myrna Kaye is a poster woman for telling the truth: bearing our souls is an essential component to creating and living a healthy life we love, in spite of our regrets and misfortunes. Life is full of ups and downs that are sometimes incredibly challenging, but it can still be full of wonder and blessings."

Esther Wright, MA
Retired Educator, Author
Laguna Woods, California

"*Mother in Name Only* chronicles the unpredictable challenges of the heroine's journey in an engrossing and masterfully crafted novel."

Gloria Waldman, PhD
Author, Journalist, Professor
Boynton Beach, Florida

"*Mother in Name Only* is a riveting book about family, love, loss and human frailty. The author whisks you along on a journey of childhood and motherhood in all its dysfunction and delight. The authenticity and animation, drama and disappointment, make this book a page-turner. This is a great read and a journey to behold. Enjoy the ride."

Diane Feen
Yoga Teacher and Freelance Writer
New York City and Boca Raton, Florida

DIANA KINGSLEY

MOTHER IN NAME ONLY

A Novel

Library of Congress Cataloging-in-Publication Data

Kingsley, Diana
Mother in Name Only: A Novel

p. cm.
Paperback ISBN: 978-1-947708-98-3
Ebook ISBN: 978-1-947708-93-8
Library of Congress Control Number: 2021923083

10 9 8 7 6 5 4 3 2 1
First Edition, October 2021

 CITRINE PUBLISHING

Brasstown, North Carolina, U.S.A.
(828) 585-7030
Publisher@CitrinePublishing.com
www.CitrinePublishing.com

ACKNOWLEDGMENTS

How can I ever forget my very good friends, who were always there for me and helped me by just listening? Suffice it to say, there are a lot of people who I truly feel have continued to support me as I flounder around, trying to express myself appropriately and do the right thing. However, of all the people who have been in my life, the most important is my father, who left me the legacy of knowing unconditional love.

This is the story of a woman who didn't know,
written by a woman who does.

PROLOGUE
YOM KIPPUR, 2004

Forgiveness. The opportunity to atone. The allure of a slate swept clean of our foibles, missteps and selfishness. It's part seduction, part devotion, part obligation and a little bit of guilt. But, I think, it is hope that brings even the most ambivalent or conflicted of my people to synagogue on Yom Kippur. We pray for another chance to do better. Collectively, we wake up on this most holy of Jewish holidays, ignore the rumblings in our stomachs caused by fasting, and prepare to go to synagogue.

I've been here in La Jolla for six months. I have no family to speak of, and I don't belong to a synagogue. Instead, I've come out to this wide gray beach. I can see from the windows of my apartment, the reason—well, one of the reasons—I'm here, instead of on Manhattan's Upper East Side, where I have lived for so many years. I love the smell and feel of being near the ocean; I love to walk barefoot in the waves as they spill onto the beach.

Today, a weekday in October, the beach is nearly deserted. Just a few weeks ago you would have found music

1

booming from radios and CD players, smells of barbecue and fried food. I also see open bottles of suntan lotion, color, laughter, shouts and the crack of the side of a hand on a volleyball. I even hear the tearful wails of cranky children, hot and tired and uncomfortably sandy. Throughout the summer this beach is crowded with bodies—tattooed and pierced—mostly lean and toasted brown, even on a weekday. Now the weekends draw a respectable crowd. The waves are speckled with surfers in gleaming black wetsuits, their bright boards slicing the curls and then bobbing in the shallows. I love crowds. It helps me to dispel, at least for a time, the emptiness that weighs me down.

It is late afternoon, and very warm. If I were home in New York City, right now, the air would be apple crisp and the sun would have set. But in California, summer waxes and wanes; it never really ends. Not like in New York, where a frigid wind racing down First Avenue can make me doubt that there is such a thing as summer.

Today I am barefoot, wearing a white cotton T-shirt and white pants rolled to the knee. The wearing of white on Yom Kippur to symbolize purity and the cleansing of our sins. It's one of the customs to which I never before subscribed, although the memory of my mother, dark hair falling against the snowy fabric of a white dress, is one I always associate with the holiday.

The Pacific is rowdy today. The salty gusts that whip my hair as I make my way across the coarse sand are the wave-making winds for which surfers pray. Sure enough, there are a few fanatics on the waves: mostly guys, although not all young, whose dedication to catching the thrill by catching the wave has steered them toward the kind of life that allows them to be in the water on a Tuesday in October. This allows me to watch them with admiration. There is a simplicity and a clarity to their joy. How does one love something so single-mindedly?

I wince as I watch two wave-riders aim for the same sweet spot on the curl of a mint-green wave. For a few seconds, the wave is in control, and the men and boards flip and spin, until it turns over and spills them into the shallows, where they rise and cheerfully shake themselves off. There is no collision, and the surfers are happy to be spilt.

I came here for that feeling. When I left my sunny little apartment about an hour ago, I could have turned toward one of the more secluded and picturesque beaches here. But I chose instead this well-used public beach, where I knew I would find the distraction I was seeking. There is something about the ocean, about its lack of concern for the troubles and desires of human beings, that I respect. I feel small here, but not insignificant. I came here to let the waves take me out of myself and away from my body for a few minutes. These last few hours before nightfall, before I can break my fast, are proving to be a challenge.

As it happened, I did not eat last night because I wasn't hungry, and then I slept, and when I woke this morning, I thought perhaps this fast was meant to be. I consider this as I continue down the beach, past the empty lifeguard stations and boarded concession stands. I swerve into the water, letting the churning remnants of waves splash up my tanned calves, and unexpectedly laugh because it feels good. I have weathered the spike of hunger that drove me from my apartment, and now I feel strong, my body light and limber.

For the past few months, I've been trying to follow a strict diet of mostly raw foods. And at the end of every day, when I have fed my body only wholesome things, I feel a small triumph. Food, and more specifically my dependence on food for comfort, was the last of my vices, the last crutch on which I leaned after decades spent on the struggle to cast away the others: a pill for anxiety, three packs of cigarettes a day, alcohol, anti-depressants. One by one, I let loose my grip on the things that helped me to survive, and it was terrifying. It was terrifying to stand alone. And now I find myself on this beach in California with no crutches left, no buffer from the feelings that threaten to overwhelm me, feelings like waves, facts I can no longer ignore. No protection.

But right now, my body feels clean and hollow, and I am thinking about dinner, or rather dinners. Food. The last buffer between what I fear to confront and the peace that I—sometimes—believe I will achieve. Have I ever felt strong enough? Weakness, I think, is one of those sins for which today I must atone.

But what is sin if not a failure to do as much good as one can? A failure to seize opportunities to do good? It's not what you do, but what you don't do that ends up making the difference. It's not what you say, but what you don't say. My life's project, I reflect, has been to not say what I know to be the truth, and the consequences of that put me alone on this beach on Yom Kippur, thinking of walking straight into those waves.

I don't know where this insight is coming from—the vast expanse of sky, the rhythm of the waves that seem to be talking to me, telling me that I sin when I fail to do good—but somehow I understand things in a different way than I did before, as if all the years of withdrawal and twelve-step programs and frustration, of transformational workshops on opening to life, and all the months of pure food and cleansing, yoga and meditation have finally paid off in clarity. By giving up all that formerly supported me, right down to food, I have gained vision, and I see what I am here to atone for. I see why things have not gone the way I expected in California.

I came to the state pumped with optimism. Recently retired, a lifelong New Yorker for whom the charms of the city had long since worn away, I closed the door to my apartment and came west. I wanted sky and clouds, water and greenery around me. I wanted this perfect California weather—not too hot during the day, cool evenings great for sleeping—I wanted to try to be close to two of my sons, and I wanted to give the third the space and time he had asked for. I wanted to get to know my grandchildren. I wanted to breathe fresh clean air and eat healthy food and sleep deeply and just feel good. I wanted to wake up to quiet, not the crash and bang of garbage trucks and jackhammers, or the screech of sirens. New York is so noisy.

But I found myself missing the noise. Waking up in my sweet, airy little apartment, decorated in shabby chic from thrift stores and consignment shops, and from which the Pacific can be seen out of every window, from my bed in the bedroom, the living room and the balcony. Still I find the silence disconcerting. It makes me feel lonely. Old wounds can't be healed so easily. And I miss working; I miss the eager gaze of students. I miss being needed. I miss taxis. I don't like driving. The challenge of getting around by car here is daunting, and I'm not ready yet for the freeway.

I have kept myself very busy here in La Jolla. I've made some friends and gotten close to my neighbors. I've been to three singles parties downtown and taken two courses at UC San Diego. I attend my twelve-step meetings regularly and have been grateful for this spiritual community. I've made one good friend, who is a native La Jollan and very involved in the community, and she's opened a lot of social opportunities for me.

I never told her about my relationship with my sons, and I always felt guilty about that. You can't have a real relationship with someone if you can't tell the truth. So I have been lonely here, isolated by a shame that keeps me from offering an authentic version of myself to friends, a shame I thought I had left behind.

Despite all that has happened in the last three years, I did have dreams, fantasies of holidays spent with all three of my boys. I imagined they would be close, all of them. I imagined their children would grow up friends, close cousins such as I never had, and that I would be Grandma to all of them. I understand now that I am not going to have much of a chance with the boys. Their wives barely talk to me.

I am not the first person to switch coasts in an attempt to switch lives, and I know I am not the first to be disappointed by the results. Your life comes with you.

I have walked further than I meant to, so lost in thought that I noticed neither the distance nor my hunger pains. The last beachcombers are far behind me, and the great ball of sun has slipped down over the horizon, leaving a golden afterglow that will remain, I know, for some time. I think I will walk a bit farther, to the next kink in the shoreline, just to see what lies beyond. And then I will turn around. Good Jewish people break their fast not at sunset, but at nightfall, which has been defined by the rabbis as one hour past sunset. By the time I walk back home, night will have officially fallen, and I will eat something, perhaps read. If I can muster the courage, I might call my boys. There is so much I want to say to them.

To ignore an opportunity to do good is a sin. I scuff my bare feet through the coarse, dark sand, simply to enjoy the sensation as I think more about this. My family is fractured. What opportunity to do good have I missed? What do my boys need from me that I can give them now? What will they accept from me?

I am approaching the place where the shoreline curves to the right around a finger of high dunes covered with beach grass. This is the furthest I've ever walked on this beach, and I feel unexpectedly excited. Whatever is around that bend, it will be something I haven't seen before. There is still that; there is still the thrill of new vistas.

Clearly that jutting cigar of dune, the first thing I notice is how littered it is on the far side. Not only human litter, although there is a fair amount of that, but ocean litter, the things the water spits back up at us: tangled, green-black clumps of seaweed and beds of sharp, cracked shells, lifeless horseshoe crabs abandoned high up on the sand, dead fish and shards of glass merely broken, not yet weathered into alluring frostiness. And even, I see with surprise and morbid curiosity, a shipwreck, the inverted hull of what appears to have been a yacht, barnacle-encrusted, riddled with large holes through which the water splashes, and even some ambitious graffiti: Remy37USMC, and Mean People Suck, and The Truth Shall Set You Free.

Indeed, I think. The truth shall set you free. I stop walking and stand in the glow of the fading day, looking around at the deserted beach, which, if not exactly pretty, is authentic. This beach is telling its truth, I think. And it is telling me to do the same.

Is that the opportunity to do good that I have neglected? The truth? What if I did? What would happen if I told everyone—my parents, my friends and colleagues—the truth about all those years when I suffered over the loss of my children? No one, not one single person, not even my therapists over the years, knows the whole truth. I have never spoken it out loud. What would happen if I did? I ask myself this question as I stand frozen at the waterline. There is nothing but horizon in my vision: sea and sky, clean and unfettered. What freedom would look like if it weren't an abstraction.

Suddenly it is clear to me what I have to do. Tell the truth. All of it. And not here, but in New York, which is where I am my most authentic. New York, imperfect and littered, like this beach. There is an empty place in that landscape exactly the shape of my life, and I am filled with longing for familiar rhythms. For reasons I'm not sure I understand, I need to tell the story in the place where it unfolded. I need the unique energy of the city of my birth. I know that I must be reminded, and provoked, in order to do this work, and here in La Jolla it is too easy to be soothed into passivity. I have to go back. I have to tell the whole story, if there is any hope for my family and for me.

Silence, too, is a sin.

CHAPTER ONE

Opening the door to my Sutton Place apartment, where I have lived for more than forty years, I wait anxiously for the elevator to deliver my son, Moses, whom I have only seen once before, thirty-five years ago. I held him in my arms, inspected him, kissed him, cradled him and asked God to protect and care for him. And God did, I think, or at least I will know in a few short moments. My heart is pounding. My face is flushed. I wait for the elevator to arrive, not sure I will be able to survive this emotion.

I try to calm myself by remembering and replaying bits and pieces of the three-way telephone conversation I had last night with Moses and his wife, Steffi. He called me "Mom." He said *I love you,* and my heart leapt with joy. But I do not expect to receive easy gifts, and I have lived so long with the secrecy, and the fear, and the shame. I have spent my son's life condemning myself, and I cannot accept that he won't do the same. This feeling does not make sense, I know. He wouldn't have searched for me simply to denounce me, I tell myself. But how could he not hate me, not be furious and angry at me for giving him away at birth?

What is he really like? I can't quite get my mind around this reality. I am about to find out what my son is like when I have wondered about this every day for thirty-five years. For thirty-five years, I have imagined him, prayed for him and sent my love out to him through the universe, trusting and believing that it would find him. I never worried about him, though. I always felt that Moses would be exceptional: successful, healthy, and happy. And from what he told me last night on the phone, I was right. My son has been extraordinarily financially successful in real estate. He is happily married to a sweet and dynamic woman with three children, my grandchildren, and has homes in New York and Arizona. And somehow I knew this. I never worried about this son I gave away in the way I have worried so much about Mitchell and Jared, his brothers. I had not a scrap of factual information, but somehow I always knew Moses was fine.

The elevator bell interrupts my thoughts. The doors slide open, and he springs out, turning to the right instead of the left, a tall and very handsome, dark-haired man bounding halfway down the carpeted hallway in the wrong direction.

"Moses!" I shout. "Is it you?"

He turns, looks at me, and without hesitation, says, "Yes, Mom. It's me!"

I cannot believe my eyes. Could this unbelievably gorgeous young man really be my thirty-five year-old ghost of a son? Is this the boy I thought of every single day? I can barely close my gaping mouth as he enters the foyer and walks into the long living room.

"Do I look like what you expected?" he asks, laughing.

I have to answer honestly. "No," I say as I close the door behind him. I can barely speak; I am so overwhelmed.

Although Moses is the same height as his biological father, my son does not have his father's large, prominent nose or broad, athletic body. Moses' nose is small and perfect, and he is slim and in great shape. Still, standing in the foyer as I study this man. I am completely filled with awe and surprise.

He looks just like Mitchell.

It has all happened so quickly. And in comparison to the gut-wrenching pain of giving him up at birth, and to the decades I spent suffering on my own, reuniting with my lost son was surprisingly easy. In the end, all it required were a few phone calls. That, and a coincidence, and the courage and determination I had never quite possessed before.

It started simply, really, when my longtime therapist told me she was closing her Manhattan practice. Lorraine knew the circumstances of Moses' birth, as did her two predecessors, mental health professionals I saw regularly over a period of thirty years. But they had consistently discouraged me from trying to find him. It would be an interruption to your son's life, I was told. He was probably well entrenched in his family, they all said in one way or another, and if he wanted to be in touch with me, he would be. So I took this advice, continually closing the door of my heart to the pain of not knowing my child. But the pain was so great, and it kept seeping out from under the door.

When Lorraine closed her Manhattan practice, I looked for another therapist and found Susan. In our initial interview, I told her about the baby I had given up for adoption more than three decades before, and how that decision had affected every aspect of my life since; how deeply I loved this lost boy and how consuming was my desire to find him. And she didn't discourage me. Instead, she told me that times had changed, that many women were looking for their birth children, and many agencies were opening up their records. Susan told me that she had lots of experience with reunion, and that she could help me.

With Susan's guidance, I contacted the adoption agency through which my son had been placed thirty-five years earlier. The social worker there gave me some specific details about Moses' adoptive family, information I would need for the next step, which was registering with a locator service. In the last decade or so, as adoption privacy laws have loosened up in response to pressure from both birth parents and adoptees, various locator services have offered assistance. She referred me to two services that would do computer searches for my son. One of them found him. It took less than a week.

What I learned later was that Moses had already been searching for me, a process he had set in motion at age fifteen, with the blessing of his adoptive parents. It was for this reason that I was able to gain access so easily to the necessary information. The social worker knew, at the time of my first inquiry, that Moses was already looking for me. And so, just a few days after I registered with the agency, while checking my messages during my lunch break, I heard the words that would reunite me with one son and distance me from two others:

Good news! We have a match. . . .

Now Moses prances through my apartment like a child in a toy store, touching things, exclaiming, looking at all the pictures on the walls. When he enters my bedroom, he is drawn immediately to a framed photo hung to the left of my bed.

"Muir Woods, California!" he cries out. "That's my favorite place, too!"

I nod, excited that we have already found common ground. I point to the framed photo hanging above the one that caught his eye.

"What do you think of this one?" I ask. "It's an abandoned schoolhouse in the middle of nowhere in Tennessee."

"It's nice," he says. "Who took it?"

I smile. "I did," I answer, "when I went on a vacation in Tennessee." I feel my throat tighten. I can't believe I'm standing here, sharing my life and memories with my lost son. Moses turns his attention back to the original photograph.

"I love Muir Woods," he says softly.

He asks me for photographs, so I go to my walk-in closet, where I keep drawers of loose photos in my father's mahogany highboy; they are mixed from many different phases of my life, and together we pick some out. We sit down at the round table in the dining area. I show him a family album, and Moses revels in seeing photos of his brothers and photos of me when I was younger.

"I can't believe I'm looking at photographs," he says, almost shouting in his enthusiasm. "I've never been interested in looking at them before."

I watch his face light up boyishly. He can't get enough of these images of a family he had only been able to imagine up until now. I show him the wedding photograph of my mother's parents, his great-grandparents, and offer to give it to him and others as well. He accepts the offer, and I am deeply moved.

Sifting through the piles of photos scattered across the table, I come across a picture of me from a Halloween party in 1965, dressed up in a rented red-and-white-polka-dotted flamenco dancing dress. Moses takes the photo from my hand.

"You're beautiful," he gasps. I smile and lean toward him to gaze at the photo, remembering the circumstances under which it had been taken.

"We threw a big party," I say. "The theme was 'Characters from the movies: Costumes Obligatory.' Eli and I came as part of the Spanish flamenco dancing troupe from the movie *Ship of Fools*." At the mention of my ex-husband's name, I glance anxiously at Moses, searching for a reaction.

Naturally, during our long initial phone call, Moses asked about his biological father. I had vowed to be honest with him, whatever the cost, and that meant reliving only some of the terrible circumstances of his conception, birth and adoption. It was impossible to tell him the complete story, to say out loud some of the series of events I had not spoken about, except with therapists, for thirty-five years. My heavy, heavy shame and guilt were a burden I had carried for decades. Until I found Susan and set in motion the process that led to this evening, I had abandoned all hope that my load would ever be lightened. But from the very first phone call to the adoption agency, I began to feel release and strength, a reserve of strength I needed to tap into again and again as I recounted to Moses some of the details of his birth.

I had told Moses about Eli, my ex-husband, and about most of our unhappy marriage. I had tried to explain how that unhappiness—year after year of living in this cold, distant, dysfunctional, loveless relationship—had led me, one late summer evening in 1965, to a dinner table with my ex-boyfriend, Alex, my first and only real boyfriend before Eli. I had explained to Moses about our non-existent relationship for more than seven years, and how what started as an innocent dinner invitation ended up with my forced sexual intimacy and rape and pregnancy, and that I believed this was the night of his conception.

It was hard enough to even admit that I made a dinner date with a former boyfriend, much less rape. I just couldn't get that word out of my mouth. I felt so very ashamed and guilty, but I had to try to tell Moses the truth: how I came home from Alex's apartment that night so fearful that I might be pregnant that I seduced my husband just in case I was. I had to tell Moses how I carried inside me both him and the shame and guilt of that deception for seven months before telling Eli the truth, and that this truth so enraged him that he immediately instigated a series of actions that led to the adoption. And although there was no DNA testing back then, the question of my baby's true father was not in dispute at the time. I believed it was Alex. I just knew it.

Still, my intuition was never confirmed or denied in any scientific way, and I wonder, when I mention Eli's name to Moses, if he is considering the murkiness of who his biological father was. It seems, though, that he is not. He believes me. Eli believed me. And I believe, have always believed, that Alex is the father of my second son.

We sit opposite each other at the round dining room table, and I have to make the greatest effort to get the words out of my mouth. I really feel speechless. I can't stop staring at his face and hoping, believing, that he will read the love and joy in my eyes. But all of my senses are off. Nothing, no book or movie or person could have prepared me for these moments.

Although dark eyes are usually very expressive, his aren't, and I can't read him. I don't know what he's thinking and feeling, but I want more than anything for him to be happy, happy to be here, happy to finally know his mother. I want more than anything for him to forgive me, and to welcome me into his life. I want Moses to be as happy with me as I am with him, and this is so much to ask, so much to even try and say, that all I can do is stare at my son and hope that he can feel my love.

Moses takes out his cell phone and calls his wife Steffi to make plans for dinner. He follows this with a call to an Italian restaurant on First Avenue. He orders a lot of food. He is wired, excited, a bundle of energy. I am numb. It is getting late, and although I don't want this night to end, don't want to take my eyes off my beautiful son, I am feeling the effects of the strain and excitement on my body. Whatever he wants to do is fine with me. There is nothing I want more, just then, than to please him and to be with him.

We taxi uptown. I wait while Moses goes in to pick up the food, and then we continue to his apartment. My heart is beating double-time, I think; beating faster than the ticker on the taxi meter. We enter this very impressive Madison Avenue cooperative and ride the elevator up to a large and classically furnished apartment. Moses and I are standing in the living room talking when Steffi arrives home. She gazes at the two of us.

"Oh," she gasps, her eyes lighting up with delight. "You look alike. You look like mother and son!" I am swooning. I am so full of joy.

While Steffi unpacks the food, Moses leads me into a bedroom where his middle son, Mickey, who had spent the evening with the family's nanny, is already asleep. I hold back, afraid to wake the child, afraid that seeing this grandchild whose existence was not even known to me forty-eight hours before will finally push me over the edge. I am poised between laughter and tears, my joy so exquisitely sharp it's almost painful. But Moses grasps my hand and pulls me into Mickey's bedroom.

"You have to meet your grandson," he whispers.

Gently, my son wakes his son. "Mickey," he says, kneeling next to the bed. "Your grandma is here." Mickey can barely keep his eyes open. I stand silently, watching as Moses climbs onto the bed next to the boy, lying on his stomach with his arm thrown over his son's chest. Moses nuzzles him and whispers again and again: "Mickey, that's **my** Mommy. My mommy is here. . . ." I can barely hold back the tears.

After dinner in the breakfast nook of the double-sized kitchen, Moses, Steffi and I adjourn to the formal living room. The adrenaline is flowing for Moses and me. We are over-energized. Steffi suggests that they show me their wedding album. As I look through, I see a young couple, formally dressed, Steffi glowing in a wedding gown uniquely and perfectly designed for this gorgeous bride. When we get to the photo of the entire room, Steffi points out her family and guests, seated on the right side of the room; my daughter-in-law is from a prominent family, and her wedding guests included several recognizable faces from national politics and the entertainment industry. On the other side, the left side, were Moses' guests, his adoptive family and friends. Moses makes me laugh as he pokes good-natured fun at his people.

"Look at that," he says, pointing to a candid shot from the reception. "Her bra strap is hanging out. Look!" He grins. "They took their disposable cameras out during the dinner. They were taking photos of the other side, of the celebrities. Isn't that awful?" We are giggling over these pictures. We are so pleased to be together.

Moses asks about my other sons, Mitchell and Jared, and my mood becomes more somber as I speak of them, of Jared's struggle to make a meaningful life for himself, and of Mitchell's battles with family relationships. I open up about the pain I have been carrying for both my boys, how I wish I could help them more, how I wish our relationships could be stronger and more open. Jared is getting married in weeks and seems to have found both a life partner and a career path in the entertainment industry to make him happy. But Mitchell, my oldest, four years older than Jared and just months older than Moses, has been burdened by so much emotional stuff he has found it difficult to work. Mitchell is a doctor, I explain to Moses. He has the ambition to help these sick people who truly need it, using his expertise to get it accomplished.

Moses is listening intently as I speak about the brothers he doesn't yet know. I tell him about Mitchell's difficulties, and his face lights up. He has an idea.

"Hey!" he says excitedly. He looks over at Steffi. "He could come with us tomorrow." Steffi does not look nearly as enthusiastic. She shakes her head slightly.

"Oh, you just want to show off," she says to her husband, but Moses pays no attention. He has already turned toward me with a grin, eyes sparkling as he explains. Tomorrow, he tells me, he and a group of friends have plans to attend the Final Four basketball tournament and have rented a small private plane to get there. They're leaving at ten a.m., and Moses thinks Mitchell might like to come along.

"We could bond," he says, his excitement building as the idea takes hold. I can see it in his eyes; he is imagining the feeling of spending time with a *brother*.

"We'd have time to get to know each other," Moses continues, "and we have the best seats. He'd love it! What's his telephone number, Mom?" he asks, turning toward me, and I feel a little thrill. I don't really hear his question. I shiver with joy whenever he calls me "Mom."

I am in a daze. It has been such a long emotionally exhausting day. I have already gotten a second and a third wind. It is nearly midnight, and I am pushing myself. Moses repeats the question.

"Mitchell has an unlisted telephone number," I tell him quietly. "It's at home."

Moses jumps to his feet. "C'mon," he says. "Let's go get it."

"I think it's too late," Steffi interjects, looking at her husband. Then they both turn and look at me.

I am thinking about the advice I got from the social worker at the adoption agency. I had called her after my first telephone conversation with Moses, to tell her about our scheduled reunion. Adopted children feel as if they've never had any control, she had told me; let him lead. So I don't say a word when Moses jumps up and heads for the door. I follow him into the elevator, into the taxi and back to the elevator in my building, then into my apartment, where Moses sits at the dining room table, and I look up Mitchell's telephone number. Let him lead.

It is now quarter to one in the morning, and Moses dials Mitchell's number. Someone picks up. Although I don't know it yet, it is my daughter-in-law, Naomi.

"Hello," Moses says, still grinning. He thinks this is a great lark, although I am starting to feel a creeping sense of dread. "This is a patient of Mitchell Kramer. Would you please put him on the phone?"

Moses waits a moment, and then looks down at the receiver. "She hung up," he informs me as he dials the number again.

Stop! I want to say. *You don't know Naomi!* But I do nothing. I sit at the table, watching. I think of the social worker's advice: Let him be in control.

Moses is murmuring into the phone, and I hear some of what he is saying: "Can Mitchell come to the phone? . . . My name is Moses. . . . Yes, I am his brother. . . . Yes, she's sitting right here. . . ." He hands me the phone, and I say hello, but Naomi doesn't.

"Does Mitchell have *another* brother?" she demands.

"Yes," I answer simply. I have no idea how to reverse what has just happened. I have no idea how to calm her down. So I answer her question. "Yes, Mitchell has another brother. His name is Moses." I hear Naomi inhale sharply.

"First you call at almost one a.m., when I just finished feeding the baby and got him to sleep." She is screaming. I can feel her fury over the phone line. "And now, you tell us you have *another* son." She stops to catch her breath. "I'm *done!*" she screams. "Done. I really don't want anything to do with you, ever again. Don't you ever call here again." Click.

I am sitting at the table, holding the phone, too exhausted to think of what to do next. My relationship with my son's wife, always troubled, has, I suspect, just been destroyed, and I don't know what to do.

"Oh no," I singsong to Moses, as I cover my face with my hands. "She hung up."

"I'll explain it to her," he says. "Let me send her an email."

He moves swiftly across the living room to my desk and sits down at my laptop. He uses my email account and my identity to write Naomi. In less than five minutes, Moses composes an email to try to give himself, as well as Naomi, an excuse in an attempt to calm her down. Also, I think it was his way to try to explain this mess to himself.

> *Moses just left my apartment after a wonderful day together learning about one another. If you were not aware, I had an extramarital relationship on one occasion that resulted in him being born approximately one year after Mitchell. . . . I am sorry if we woke you and your family, but I only allowed him to because he explained that the plane he chartered was leaving at ten a.m. and I thought Mitchell would have wanted to meet his brother. . . .*
>
> *I am so sorry to upset you.*

The email is sent, Moses and I say our goodbyes, and I go to bed. My sense of foreboding, of the entire truth of the untold rape, keeps me awake throughout the night. When I rise in the morning, it is confirmed by an enraged response from Naomi, ending with the words:

> *When Mitchell is ready to have a relationship with you again, he will contact you. I am done.*

I am stung, destroyed, by the depth of Naomi's rage, and by worry for Mitchell. But I have, at this moment, a more pressing concern. I am afraid that Mitchell will talk to his brother Jared before I have a chance to tell him about the existence of Moses. I am anxious about how the facts might get twisted. I want to tell him about Moses myself. I want to try and do a better job announcing my long-lost son to Jared than I did to Mitchell.

Telling Jared about Moses was something I wanted to do and would do. I would never have elected to have Moses call Mitchell after midnight and wake up the family. Moses was so excited about our reunion and having a brother that he did not think about the time or the consequences. He only thought about announcing his existence to a biological brother. Telling Mitchell via telephone about Moses was not something I wanted to happen. So I sit at the computer and compose an email to Jared and his fiancée.

I need you to know that when Mitchell was three months old, I met up with an old ex-boyfriend, and I got pregnant. The son was given up for adoption. . . .

I met him last night for the first time, and I'm so very impressed with his good luck in life. He is incredibly successful, married and has three young children. He wants to be part of our family. Please advise me how to handle this delicate situation with you. I am very anxious to do the right thing.

I send the email and leave for work, feeling sick with concern for all of my sons.

I check my messages on my mid-morning break, and there is a message from Mitchell.

"Do *not* tell Jared," he says to my machine. "Jared is getting married soon. He needs to concentrate on his marriage, not on some long-lost brother. If you tell Jared about this 'brother,'" Mitchell says to my machine, "*I will never speak to you again.*"

But, of course, it was already too late. And that message, left on my answering machine more than three years ago, was the last time I heard my son Mitchell's voice. He kept his word. To this day, he does not speak to me.

That evening, that reunion, which started as a trip to paradise and an answer to my prayers, ended with a nightmare of separation that would last up until the present moment. Mitchell and Naomi stopped talking to me entirely, and I'm not allowed to see my two grandchildren. Three years have passed and the situation remains the same. Jared and Jane and my newest grandson, Louis, are distant. Jared has asked me only once, briefly, about Moses. And Moses has had so many things to learn, stories to tell and hear, and people to meet, including Alex and his wife. Yet somehow, with Moses, the close relationship about which I fantasized for so many years has yet to develop.

I was raised by a woman who did not want to be a mother and did not bother to hide that fact from her daughters: *I'm a mother in name only,* she would say, almost proudly, to my sister and me, and she would prove it when we were teenagers by leaving us one summer afternoon, taking all our father's hidden cash and leaving only a cryptic, unapologetic note. Like daughters everywhere raised by reluctant mothers, I swore I would be different. But perhaps it was inevitable that I would not be able to give to my sons all they needed from a mother. I had no skills, no model, no way at all to know what a good mother did. I was an immature twenty-six-year-old when I had my first son. But unlike my mother, I wanted, and still want, to do better.

I want to explain some things to my sons. It starts right now, right here, as I sit at this keyboard, alone, a mother without her sons, a mother in name only.

CHAPTER TWO

She seemed like a wicked woman. I did not want to be in that house. I wanted to disappear. So many ugly feelings. So much angst. I wanted to come to my father's rescue, but I was only in my first years of being a teenager and I didn't think I could. *Little girls should be seen and not heard* my mother had drilled into us, one of the many clichés she relied on. *A fool and his money are soon parted* she might say when denying us some request she deemed too frivolous an expense. But I didn't know the platitudes by which my mother lived were clichés. I thought she invented them.

In later years, when she came to visit in Manhattan, my mother would take all the credit for my decorating sense, good taste and color coordination. *The apple doesn't fall far from the tree!* she'd exclaim. But by then I knew she hadn't an original thought in her head.

But for all of my childhood, my mother made the rules and we followed them. The day she left, leaving behind a note that said *I won't be back; I'll be in touch; I can't take it anymore,* the first thing I felt was joy—wild, dangerous happiness. I was secretly happy to be free of the dragon.

She lives in Boca, in a one-bedroom rental in Sunrise City. My Uncle Steven helped her find it after she retired from Saks. He found it in the local newspaper. She lives on social security and some small investments. I think Steven decided it made more sense to move her from California to Florida than to endure her regular complaints about loneliness: *I'm all alone,* she would say to him in frequent telephone calls, *just like a dog,* followed by a big sigh. I suppose she decided that, since she had always looked after him, it was Steven's obligation to take care of his big sister.

Steven was the one of my mother's siblings with whom she felt the slightest bit of affinity. Like her, he dreamed of escaping Vermont, and acted on his dream by eloping at age eighteen with Lorraine, his young bride. The newlyweds made their way to Brooklyn, where my parents, almost newlyweds themselves, took them in. And although it was my father who helped Steven buy his first car and get his first job, my mother somehow remembered the aid as being rendered by her and her alone. Never one to forget a debt, she convinced herself that Steven still owed her something.

She dresses in white clothing—polyester pedal pushers and short sleeved blouses, and usually a Chesterfield-colored vest. She covers her gray with a light brown rinse and wears it short. She doesn't have a suntan, as she knows that the sun ages you prematurely. She seems tiny to me; a small woman, still thin, who from the back looks like a boy. She looks nothing like the mother I keep alive in my imagination; the woman I conjure up when I think of my mother as tall and ferocious, with medium brown hair and high heeled pumps; red lipstick and pearl earrings. As unimaginable as it seems, I know it to be true: the woman of my imagination is gone, replaced by this old lady among old ladies. The woman who appropriated clichés as if they were original thinking has faded; faded into just another old lady in Sunrise City.

She calls the screened porch tacked to the back of her unit her "studio," and she fancies herself an artist. She paints passable copies of the masterpieces of great artists. Once I asked her why she had stopped making paintings of her own vision. She looked at me blankly.

"I paint the best," she answered, nodding toward the Edward Hopper she was currently reproducing. "One isn't served by embracing mediocrity."

On the dining room wall in my apartment in New York hangs an example of my mother's "mediocrity." An original painting she did while we were living in Roslyn, I think. I found it in the back of a closet in the Flatbush apartment, the last place where she actually lived with us. It is a study of three females—a mother and two daughters. All are dark-haired, and each wears a white dress that stands out dramatically against a deep blue background. It is a portrait of us, I can only presume; my mother, Sandra and me, abandoned to the back of a closet, like foreshadowing. I suppose my mother believed it to be mediocre.

I could only smile at my mother's reasoning. It was so like her—both self-inflating and self-protective. I sometimes wondered if my mother was really meant to be Jewish. She didn't even look Jewish, but she did wear a chai around her neck. For luck, she said, and to proclaim her Judaism. I believe she was proud to be Jewish. In fact, one of her pet peeves was the use of the shortened word "Jew" to speak of her people. She insisted that we always use the complete word—"Jewish"— and we did.

But still, sometimes, to prove her point, her reasoning could be positively contorted, although she would insist it made perfect sense. She would have made an excellent

Christian Scientist: to name it is to claim it. To be the best, one merely has to copy the best.

I cannot think of my mother without her fox stole. Every picture I can conjure of her, as well as a remarkable number of the photos I have of her, feature her posed and smiling and, it seems, arranging her body so that her fox stole is well displayed.

It was the type of accessory that would be considered vulgar now, a double length of red fox fur with tails and heads—featuring glass eyes even—still dangling at either end. Even in the summer heat, my mother wore that stole proudly. At first, it was because she didn't have a fur coat to show off, so she made double use of that stole. But even later, during the years in Roslyn, when my father could finally buy her that coat, she still would toss her fox around her neck with a certain flair that told me she loved it. I think she just liked the way it looked on her, like an aviator, like an heiress. Sometimes when she was readying herself to go out for the evening, I would watch her as she checked her reflection, patted her brown hair into place, tested that her screw-back earrings were secure and her lipstick unsmudged, before lovingly winding the fox stole around her neck and whispering to herself: *Perfect!*

Perfection was the standard that guided my mother; an idea she held in her imagination of the kind of life to which she was entitled: perfect husband, perfect children, perfect figure, perfect house. She married a college-educated Jewish professional, and for awhile, until it all went awry, I think she believed in him, I think she believed he was going to be everything she hoped for. She never saw my father for who he was—well meaning and sometimes childlike, impulsive, generous and overly optimistic—and she never forgave him for not being who she thought he could be, for not being perfect.

I don't think my father has ever stopped loving her, and sometimes I think she still loves him. But if I have learned anything from studying my parents' marriage, it is this: love is not the umbrella that encompasses everything else. The "everything else" matters, maybe even more than the love.

She hated sex. I could tell this even before I had a clear idea of what sex was, of what went on behind the closed door of my parents' bedroom. But for all of my father's affability, his freely given hugs and caresses and kisses, she responded with a tightness of body, straight-backed and stiff-armed, she would step away from his advances, barely controlling her expression, which seemed sometimes, when she looked at my father, to be disapproving. Proud of her "perfect" posture, she held her body rigid and had a way of pulling away from my father's affection; she never pushed him away, but would withdraw without bending, in one smooth, unyielding motion.

Later, when Sandra and I were teenage girls grappling with our own emerging sexuality, our mother abandoned subtlety and nonverbal cues. She described the relations between men and women as disgusting, primitive, but unavoidable in the life of a good wife. If my father was late getting home, she could sometimes become so angry and jealous that she would confront him as soon as he came in the front door. *Were you with another woman?* she would ask, her voice icy with contempt. And he would simply stare at her, his sadness lying just beneath impatience and anger.

My mother was not flexible, either in body or spirit. She could not adapt to the life she had, but instead tried and tried and tried to make it the life she wanted. She wanted perfect daughters. She wanted to be the perfect mother. I think she thought she was.

I give you girls everything, she would snap at us sometimes when she was annoyed. And she did give us a lot of the things she thought we needed. Lessons—piano, dance and elocution throughout most my childhood; expensive clothes, private schools—which I didn't want—medical specialists. When there was a social event at our synagogue or some extracurricular activity at our schools, she made sure we attended, well-dressed and with everything we needed. But I never felt like she saw us. She would look at her daughters and check off what mattered to her: were we dressed neatly? Was our hair combed? Her eyes would dart to our small white hands, checking to make sure there was no grime under our nails. Were we quiet and tidy and polite?

But we could never live up to the idea she had of who we should be; who we could be, if only we would behave, cooperate, stop challenging her authority. *Take them away!* she would sometimes shout at my father, dismissing Sandra and me with a sweep of her arm. *I can't take care of them.* And I knew then that I was nothing more than an irritant to my mother, one she tolerated most of the time, to her credit, as she saw it. I can still relive those moments with awesome specificity: the sharp edge of her voice in contrast to the gracefulness of her arm. But now, when I pull that memory to the surface, it is her face that swims before my mind's eye, and what I can see now—is that my mother was in pain.

I'm having heart palpitations! A racing heart was one of her trump cards when we upset her; her health, her weight and the signs and signals of her body her main concern. Years after she stopped being my mother in any mean- ingful way, during the time when my marriage to Eli was breaking up, she sent me an odd letter; a typically awkward attempt at motherly advice long after it would or could have been welcome. What I remember about that letter is that it contained a list of what she thought should have been my priorities, and that at the top of that list, above "husband," "children," and "home," were the words "your health."

She was before her time in many ways. She drank eight glasses of water a day, one cup of hot water with lemon in the morning, which she called "a hot shower, but on the inside." The most she ever drank was a sip or two of an alcoholic beverage. She never smoked cigarettes, and detested the Chesterfields my father smoked constantly. She took vitamins, never left the house until her hair was completely dry, and in chilly weather she made sure her neck was always wrapped.

She planned well-balanced meals for her family, taking the food pyramid seriously but making adjustments that today are recommendations: small portions of lean meats, baked potato or, better yet, baked yam with no butter or salt, fresh vegetables lightly steamed. Oatmeal for breakfast. No candy.

But she liked candy. She would never admit it, but whenever my mother entertained, she would buy a box of assorted chocolates and, when the party was over, hide the leftovers from Sandra and me and treat herself to not more than one piece a day. We knew she did this, and it became our project to find the hidden candy. I remember a canasta party my mother threw one winter in Roslyn. It must have been near Valentine's Day, because the candy was packaged in a heart-shaped box covered with red foil and velvet ribbon. It was beautiful, a Barracini's deluxe assortment. I wanted to hold the box nearly as much as I wanted to taste the chocolate.

It was an afternoon party, and we had been sent upstairs for the duration. I remember it was a clear and sunny afternoon, and I wanted to be outside, but my mother, ever vigilant about the possibility that we might catch cold, had ordered us to stay in our rooms. As the sound of the party breaking up drifted up the stairs, Sandra and I emerged and sat on the floor in the hallway, listening to the cultured tenor of my mother's voice, still revealing her Vermont accent, saying goodbye to her guests.

I had seen the box of candy that morning, laid out on the kitchen counter with all the other party food, and the image had occupied me all afternoon. As soon as we heard the final guest leave, my sister and I bounced down the stairs, happy to be released from our afternoon's incarceration. My father was in the living room, sipping a cocktail, and he greeted us with typical delight.

"Girls!" he shouted. "Where have you been?" As if he didn't know. I could never decide if my father knew the severity of my mother's demands and chose to avoid conflict, or if he genuinely didn't realize what was going on. Had he really not known that we had been ordered upstairs? Had he really just forgotten about us for the past three hours? Or did he know my mother's rules, and comply with them by his silence? Now I am disturbed by either possible truth. But then, I just wanted chocolate.

Sandra ran to my father's open arms, but I swerved toward the kitchen, where my mother was with the maid, putting away the party food.

"Mom?" I said, as sweetly as I could. "Could I have a piece of candy?"

"No," she answered, without even looking at me. "There's none left." I could see the box on the counter, the beribboned lid lying beside the heart shaped box with its little compartments molded of brown plastic to the exact shape of the sweetness it held. It was more than half full of succulent, creamy chocolates filled with, I knew, delicious things I rarely tasted: maple whip and peppermint creams; almonds and caramel and crunchy, buttery sweetmeats. All within reach, and all denied to me. *There's none left* she said, even though she knew I could see, right in front of me, what she wouldn't let me have.

The next day I came home from school and searched that house until I found the candy. My mother was out, and the maid ignored me as I pulled open drawers, climbed on chairs to check the high shelves of closets, tipped the lids off hat boxes and removed every pillow and cushion from the living room furniture. I found it, finally, in the hamper in the hall linen closet, at the bottom of the dirty clothes.

"Sandra!" I called triumphantly. "Sandra!" When my sister finally appeared, I pointed to the beribboned scarlet box at the bottom of the hamper. She made a little noise, half fear and half desire.

"She said there was none left," I said, more to myself than to Sandra. I leaned into the hamper and withdrew the box, gently lifting the lid to reveal more than half of the assortment, each candy nestled safely in its customized compartment. "Liar."

I was staring at the chocolate. She would tell us there was none left. Keep it all for herself. That my mother wanted to save the sweetest, best things for herself—candy, clothes, our father's love—was a concept I was used to. But to *lie*; to lie when she was always telling us that we had to be *better* than low-class people who did low-class things like lying, hit me at that moment, standing in the bathroom holding the evidence of her selfishness and lack of class, as shameful. I was ashamed for my mother. I didn't understand yet concepts like ethics and hypocrisy. I just knew this was wrong.

"We can't eat it," Sandra whispered. "She'll be so angry."

"Get the sewing kit," I said to my sister, pointing toward the Singer sewing machine, where my mother kept her supplies for sewing and mending. Sandra, always willing to concede the ringleader role to me, obediently crossed the hall to fetch it.

"What do you want it for?" she asked, as I rummaged through the tangle of thread, fabric scraps, random buttons and small silver thimbles. It was so typical of my mother, who was adamant that her family and her home appear, always, neat and well organized. Any aspect of her life that could be seen by others had to be, always, perfect. But below the surface, in the bedroom drawers and closets, under the beds and behind the furniture, was chaos. If it didn't show, she didn't care about it. She didn't care about the chaos in our minds, the longing in our hearts. But our hair always needed to be combed. I extracted, finally, from the chaos that was my mother's sewing kit, a straight pin, and showed it to Sandra.

"What's it for?" she whispered, as if I were going to use it to perform magic. I reached for the box of candy that I had left balanced on the lip of the sink. I opened the box.

"We can check the centers," I said. "Get the ones we like. She won't know." I chose a piece of candy, a nondescript rectangle covered in dark chocolate. Feeling important, like a surgeon or a jewel thief, I turned over the candy and gently inserted the pin into the center. Sandra watched in awe as I withdrew the pin, looked at it, sniffed it and then wrinkled my nose.

"It's orange," I said. "One of those orange jelly things."

"I hate those," Sandra said.

"Me too," I agreed. I showed Sandra the bottom of the chocolate, where the pinhole was visible only to a knowing eye. "See?" I said. "She'll never know."

When I put the pin through what turned out to be a chocolate-covered cherry, we had a moment of panic as the sweet red syrup leaked out. Sandra, ever eager to avoid conflict, chose to eat the evidence. But what she really wanted was a fudge-filled candy, a truffle, and after a few more pinpricks, I found her what she wanted.

"I can't," she said, stepping away from the offered candy, her brown eyes wide with fear. "She'll notice!" she whispered anxiously.

"No she won't," I said, although I knew she would. She had probably counted the remaining candies and planned the order and frequency with which she would consume them, before she chose the hiding place. "Eat it," I said, holding the chocolate out to Sandra and squeezing it slightly so that it lost its shape. "See. Now you have to eat it. She'll see someone touched it." My sister conceded, as she often did as the unwilling accomplice in my rebellious schemes, and ate her truffle hungrily.

My preference was nut clusters, easily identified. I didn't need the pin to find my favorites, and I ate every single one in that box, knowing, with each bite, that my mother would notice the disappearance of all the chocolates containing nuts and would know exactly what happened. And thinking, with each bite: *She shouldn't have lied.*

She overdressed us, insisting on full rain gear if there was even the smallest chance of a shower, and we wore sturdy oxford shoes—*to prevent weak ankles*, she would say—and heavy winter coats long into spring, far past the time when all of our friends were allowed to trade them for lighter jackets. She served us vitamin-rich foods we didn't like—lamb chops, liver, kale and broccoli—because she was convinced of their cold-prevention properties. Some years she even insisted we get monthly B12 shots, which, in the 1940s and 1950s, was akin to black magic.

It seemed, though, that my mother was torturing herself as much as us. Monitoring our health so vigilantly meant keeping us inside and close to her as much as possible. And she didn't really want us close to her.

Not all women are meant to be mothers. Sometimes, when I am able to put aside the anger and shame that thinking of my mother always evokes—anger, because I was a girl who desperately needed to know I was loved, raised by a woman who withheld love the same way she withheld candy; and shame because I can't, even now, completely forgive her—sometimes I can think of my mother as a woman woefully miscast. She didn't want to be a mother.

For three years when I was in middle school, we lived in Roslyn, New York, a mostly Jewish, upper middle class community on the north shore of Long Island, and if there was any time in my childhood when my mother was happy, that was it. Thinking back on that time now, I realize this: the pleasure my mother took in her house, the lavish attention she gave it, the pride she took in showing it off and bragging about it, mirrors the behavior of a mother for her beloved children. For many women, motherhood is the goal. For my mother, it was a house. Because of who she was and the age in which she lived, she needed the husband to get the house, and the children to appease the husband. She loved her house. She never recovered from losing it.

The house my father bought her was a four-bedroom Tudor with a large yard, set back from the street on a quiet block of similar neat and roomy homes. An inherently thrifty (one might even say cheap) woman, my mother spared no expense in decorating her house. Except for some heirloom pieces, we took nothing from the apartment in Brooklyn when we moved to the house.

She favored expensive wallpaper rather than paint or paneling: old-fashioned textured ivory for the living room, stripes in the kitchen, intricately designed forest green embossed paper in her formal dining room. Sandra and I, for the first time, had separate bedrooms in which everything matched: bedspreads and curtains coordinated with appropriately girlish wallpaper and matching carpeting. And, of course, a skirted dressing room table for each of us.

We had a live-in maid in Roslyn, and my parents entertained frequently. My mother was active in the Sisterhood at our temple, and graced my father's arm regularly at social functions. Sandra and I were doing well in a good public school and involved after school with our friends and activities, so she didn't have very much to do with us. By that time, this state of affairs satisfied all of us.

For those three years in Roslyn, my mother was, I believe, as happy as she was capable of being.

She never recovered from the loss of her house, and her life since then has been a case study in the consequences of achieving one's desire, and then losing it. She designed her life to fill a small and rigid niche. She wanted to be a Jewish matriarch, and her house was the first concrete step toward that goal. One might argue that her children qualified as the first step; a woman cannot be a matriarch without a family to command, after all. But we were not a credit to her, the way her house was. She believed her value was reflected in the neatness of her lawn and the obsequiousness of her live-in help.

Losing the house was my mother's tragedy. It shattered the image she had of herself, of who she thought she could be, and she had nothing to replace it. And it was evidence of my father's inadequacy and dishonesty. He promised her a certain kind of life, and he failed to keep that promise. The day my mother told Sandra and me that we were moving, her skin was ashen, and her hands trembling. It is one of the few times I can remember her being unwilling to make eye contact.

"We've had a reverse of finances," was all she said. That's all I knew.

Vermont's Jewish community at the turn of the twentieth century was small and very protective of itself, a proud but tense fellowship of mostly Eastern European and Russian families who found themselves, in the haphazard way immigrants often do, occupying a tiny piece of this modest and otherwise homogeneous state. My grandfather, Aaron Jacobs, emigrated from Russia with his young wife and the nimble fingers of an expert tailor. I have never heard an explanation for why Aaron chose to settle in Vermont, but I imagine his reasons were not much different from those of most immigrants: perhaps he had a sponsor there, or a family member, or a promise of a job. Whatever the reason, there were enough Jewish families already established to provide the Jacobs both the necessary sense of belonging and customers in need of Aaron's sewing skills. So they stayed.

They had five children in rapid succession; that the first three were girls must have caused my grandparents no small amount of consternation, as well as the pity of their neighbors. But they persevered and were rewarded finally with two sons: my uncles Howard and Steven. The family prospered, through hard work and thrift and the micromanagement my grandmother was known for.

Just as I'm sure it was difficult for my mother to imagine her mother as a girl—innocent, vulnerable, even at times silly—I struggle to place my mother in the context of her childhood. This is largely because, except for the occasional offhand remark, usually derisive, she has never spoken of that time of her life. When she left Vermont for what she expected to be the excitement and sophistication of a big, important city—Philadelphia must have seemed like Mecca to a girl like the one I think she was—she left behind the girl she had been when she lived there and she never reclaimed her, or wanted to, as far as I can tell. But understanding my mother, a laughably impossible task I feel compelled to attempt anyway, is integral to understanding me.

I picture her as a girl, at once insider and outsider in her city, where her tightly knit community kept her safe but stifled, and in her home, where she was the middle child of five, two older sisters and two younger brothers, siblings who logically paired up by age and gender, leaving her the odd girl out. And she was an odd girl: simple friendliness came hard to her. She seemed always to be looking past where she was, toward something more *appropriate* for the kind of girl she imagined herself to be. *Appropriateness* was a quality my mother valued throughout her life, although I'm not sure she could have defined it. What she did know was that the insular and gossipy Jewish community was not an appropriate place for a girl with dreams, a girl who loved fashion, and music, a girl who held certain beliefs about herself that could not be expressed, much less acted upon, in Vermont.

My grandmother was known as the General, a Jewish matriarch who ruled her family with the proverbial iron fist. In photos I have of her, she is a boxy woman with a steel gray bun, standing unsmiling next to my grandfather. *She swept the dirt*, my mother used to say about her admiringly, as a way of describing the sanitary state of the family homestead.

Rachel, my mother's oldest sister, emulated her mother to such a degree that she was known as the Sergeant. My mother, domineering herself but lacking any stature in her family, must have been infuriated by the constant commands and criticism coming at her not only from a mother she was obligated to obey, but from an older sister too. She escaped by finishing her high school coursework by age sixteen, leaving her free to take classes at the University of Vermont while still technically a high school student. And it was there that she met Jack Fein.

Jack Fein was such a mythic figure of my childhood, I sometimes imagined him as my other father, my alternate father, representing for me, just as he did for my mother, the alternate life we both could have had. He was a first-year medical student when my mother was a high school senior, a tall, dark-haired Jewish boy from a wealthy New Jersey family. My mother dated him for a year, and the potential of that relationship, more than its reality, left an indelible impression on her, and in turn on me. In tender moments and angry ones; during times when my mother was trying, in her awkward fashion, to be motherly by giving me advice, and at others, far more frequent, when she was belittling me for my bad choices or lack of class, when she was disappointed in me or angry at my father or just frustrated with her life, my mother would remind us: *I could have married a doctor.*

I would like to say that the degree to which Jewish families exalted medical doctors—Jewish ones, of course, and especially as husbands for their daughters—has mellowed in the decades since my mother dated Jack Fein, but I don't believe it has. Perhaps the impulse has adapted to the times in that Jewish parents pressure their daughters as well as their sons to *become* doctors, but if, after becoming an MD she marries one, the Jewish daughter has truly achieved success.

It's not pure snobbishness; of course it isn't. As a people denied both security and respect throughout history, the premium placed on professional careers—medicine first, of course, but law is good, and any white-collar employment into which a child successfully lands will allow most Jewish parents to sleep easily—is rooted in the deep-seated desire that their children be safe in a world that has proven to be otherwise for Jewish people. *I could have married a doctor!* she would remind us, a mantra that was particularly hurtful in its subtext: *I could have had better than this*; better cars, better clothes, better vacations, better places to live, better invitations, a better husband, better daughters. All of this, if only she had married Jack Fein.

I remember one particularly vicious argument I had with my mother. It was probably during her last year with us, when her unhappiness translated into constant complaining and barely concealed fury. She was so bitter about our family's financial situation, so angry at my father for causing it and so devastated at being back in Brooklyn after three short years in her beloved Roslyn Tudor; and this overwhelming desolation translated, as was my mother's way, into meanness. She honestly didn't have any other way to be.

What could we have been arguing about that day? My friends, whom she didn't like? My appetite, because she was afraid I would get fat? My grades? She didn't care how I was doing in school. My father's attention? She didn't want it by then. Most likely it was something minor: too much time on the telephone, a towel left on the bathroom floor. Whatever it was, my mother seized on it as an opportunity to release all the toxicity of her unhappiness, and how all of this unhappiness was the result of her husband and children, who were careless and common and trying to bring her down to their level. Although I can no longer remember the specifics of the argument, my mother's snarl as she belittled me is indelible. And as she recited the litany of my inadequacies, her face twisted with fury, her arm sweeping to take in the "slum" we were forcing her to live in, I felt my own rage mounting. I was tired of this, tired of her—this devil masquerading as a mother.

"You know. . . ." She had finally reached the end, and I swear she was breathing heavily, winded by the force of her discontent, embodied at that moment by me, a fifteen-year-old girl already made weary from their emotional assaults. You know, I could have married a doctor."

I had heard that line dozens of times, but it was not until this moment that it occurred to me to ask why she hadn't.

"So why didn't you?" I asked, not even trying to temper the contempt I felt. I looked up and into her eyes defiantly, and saw in them something that instantly changed my contempt to pity. My mother's face had gone white, as had the knuckles of her right hand, which gripped the back of a straight chair as if for balance. And she wouldn't hold my gaze. I think she mumbled some response, but it didn't matter. The few seconds during which our eyes were locked had given me the answer to the question of why my mother hadn't married Jack Fein and become a doctor's wife.

He hadn't asked.

So maybe it was a broken-hearted girl who arrived in Philadelphia in the fall of 1938. A girl who had had her eyes on the prize, her fingers wrapped around the golden ring, her resurrection imminent but not to be achieved; from cold, dreary Vermont and from the obscurity of being the middle child in a family equally cold and dreary. Jack Fein didn't love her. Or he did love her, but he couldn't choose her. Was my mother a victim of the same snobbishness that would, later in her life cause her to view her husband and daughters as, alternately, her project or her burden? Was she attracted to what Jack Fein offered, or did she really love him?

Were I to pick up the phone and dial my mother in Boca to ask her these questions, I honestly don't believe she could answer them. She has mastered the art of revision. She is an unreliable source. So I must tease out her narrative as best I can, laying out the possibilities and evaluating their probability, only to discover the impossibility of the endeavor.

Perhaps my mother's heart was broken at age eighteen, and the consequence of that trauma is that she could never love again—not my father and not my sister and not me.

Or maybe it was a sick girl who moved into a rooming house near Rittenhouse Square—"a residence for young women of good families" was how she described it in a letter to Steven, "in one of the city's finest neighborhoods"—a teenager moving irrevocably, like a lamb to the slaughter, toward a psychotic break. With so many things new and unfamiliar to her, perhaps she did not recognize the malfunctioning of her mind as a problem. Perhaps she thought it merely another facet of her new life: her first time away from any member of her family; first time south of Boston; the first time she had ever lived outside of a Jewish community. I imagine she was alone mostly. In later life, she would not be a woman who made friends easily or sought out the company of other women, and I suspect that was always an aspect of her personality. I suspect also that she enjoyed the solitude; that it felt triumphant to her after eighteen years spent under the scrutiny of her mother, the General, and her sister, the Sergeant. And so, if there were subtle changes in her perception of herself and of the world around her, if she experienced a strong emotion, it could have been fear. It could even be fear seven months after her arrival, when she met my father on the ground floor of John Wanamaker's Department Store, where she had gone to see the famous bronze eagle flap its wings, something it did not actually do.

Either one of these narratives—the broken-hearted girl, the sick girl—works toward helping me to understand the woman I actually knew, the woman who suffered from perhaps the most debilitating handicap of all: an inability to love. But these are stories. I made them up. The truth exists; the truth resides right now in a one-bedroom condo in Boca, forever locked away and denied to me. So I am writing the history she won't share, because doing so satisfies me more than what was probably the truth—that she took her father's money, but never used it to pay tuition.

It is true that my mother worked at John Wanamaker's Department Store, located kitty corner from Philadelphia's City Hall, at the end of Market Street. It is true that she sold ladies' hats. This I know because it is behind the hat counter where my father first spotted her. He was a twenty-three-year old bachelor, a federal employee recently transferred to Pennsylvania. He knew no one in the city, and my father was and remains a social animal and an unapologetic flirt.

It was her confidence that first attracted him, I would guess. And her pretty face. She could not have been more unlike his sisters—giggly, doting women dedicated to homemaking, women who had never held a paying job, with no plans to change that status. He watched her modeling hats for customers who drifted to her counter, noting that every style looked attractive on her. He thought she was older than her almost twenty years, maybe even older than him. The idea of a sophisticated older woman, a career girl, titillated him.

Two days later, he saw her again. He had returned to the store with some vague notion that maybe his sisters would each like a new hat. He entered the ground floor lobby through the Market Street door, stopping for a moment to admire the dramatic space before him. The lobby of John Wanamaker's Department Store, and specifically the bronze statue of an eagle—finely detailed and as large as an automobile—that dominated it, had become a Philadelphia landmark, as tourist-worthy as the Liberty Bell itself, and more valued by native Philadelphians, who saw the eagle more often than any of the historic sites.

The six, stacked floors of the Wanamaker building were designed to work as rectangular frames around a central atrium, with the bronze eagle center in the exact middle of the airy, sparsely furnished lobby. Shoppers entering the lobby were confronted with what seemed like acres of marble flooring, polished to a high shine. Next their eyes would be inevitably drawn to the eagle sculpture, and after that had been examined, necks inevitably craned. It was an irresistible urge; no doubt the architects had counted on this. Crane your neck back, and you could see the colorful edges of each of the five retail floors above. But even more interesting were the customers leaning over one of the four-foot walls that divided store and air, looking down at their fellow shoppers as they scurried across the lobby, or stopped to stare at the eagle, or looked up. I am certain my father looked up. He probably even waved if there was a pretty girl leaning over the wall and smiling.

My mother, I am equally certain, did not look up.

My father did not have to make his way upstairs to the accessories department and then wait quietly at the hat counter while my mother took care of customers. She was there in the lobby, staring fixedly at the eagle, so intently that my father must have followed her gaze, perplexed as to what could be so interesting.

"What's so interesting?" he asked his future wife. He had positioned himself directly in front of her, momentarily blocking her view of the eagle.

"What time is it?" she asked my father. He glanced at his watch.

"Just before five," he answered. She still hadn't looked directly at him.

My mother ordinarily worked eleven a.m. to seven p.m., with a half-hour meal break, which she usually took around three o'clock. But on the day she met my father, despite the hunger pangs she must have been feeling, she put off her break until four forty-five p.m., specifically so she could see the eagle flap its wings.

The accessories department, on the fourth floor, was located right next to the cosmetics and skin care counters, which were remarkably busy especially in contrast to the rather sluggish commerce which occurred in accessories, particularly hats. Consequently, my mother spent a fair amount of time, after she neatened the displays of hats, disrupted by try-ons, and reorganized the small selection of leather and silk gloves the manager had pressed on her, insisting that ladies who buy hats always want gloves; after she'd cleaned any smudges off the glass and re-checked her handwritten sales records, she often sat quietly behind her counter and watched the cosmetics girls bustle about. They wore white lab coats over their dark, broad-shouldered suits, and a lot of make-up, and their customers were always the best-dressed women who swept onto the cosmetics floor, tried samples and asked questions and always bought something. My mother, who must have often been bored behind the ladies' hats counter and who modeled more hats than she sold, probably watched the cosmetics girls with envy.

It was one of the pretty and professional cosmetics girls who talked most often with my mother during slow periods when both of them leaned lazily over their counters, being careful not to smudge their polished glass. And it was she who told my mother that she must see the sight of the eagle flapping its wings. It was a tradition, she said; people came through the lobby at five o'clock specifically to see it. Everyone came, she said, inspiring in my mother the fierce desire to be a part of "everyone."

"What's so interesting?" my father asked again. My mother gestured toward the eagle.

"He's going to flap his wings," my mother answered. "At five o'clock. I don't want to miss it."

My father looked from Lillian Jacobs's smooth and pretty face to the large bronze eagle, which looked as solid and immovable as a meteor.

"I don't think so," he said. He walked the few steps from where they stood to stand in the space just beneath the eagle's folded wing. "Come here," he gestured. My mother looked nervously at the security guard and then stood beside my father. He pointed above their heads to the point where the wing joined the eagle body. "Look."

He placed his hands gently on her cheeks and tilted her head back.

"See? No hinges. No joints. It's one solid piece of bronze." My father laughed. "Who told you those wings flap?" he asked. And he looked into her face to see the last traces of childlike wonder draining away, to be replaced by disappointment. He couldn't know it then, but disappointment was to be my mother's official position in all dealings she would have with him as his wife.

Perhaps my father thought that he could show her amazing things—the store he had discovered on Spruce Street that made scented soaps in dozens of colors and varieties, the mirrored ball hanging from the ceiling of the Philadelphia Dance Club that twirled multi-colored stars out over the dancers and the orchestra—and bring back that unguarded, open expression of which he had had only a fleeting glimpse. But if he believed that, he was wrong.

"Nobody," my mother answered quietly in response to his question. "I just thought— maybe. . . ." Her voice trailed off, and then she straightened her posture and threw her head back. "Nobody important."

"How about a cup of coffee?" my father asked.

"No, thank you," she would have responded, always polite to strangers. She had to get back to the accessories department.

"Good!" my father said, enthusiastic and rakish, as he always was with pretty girls. "Dinner is a better idea. What time do you get off? Seven right? Seven it is. I'll meet you right here at seven. Now, I was wondering how you feel about chow mein, because there's a very nice place run by good people, good Chinese people, you know? And not very far from here."

My mother must have looked incredulously at this fast talking young man with the prematurely receding hairline and the wire-framed glasses, dressed nattily in a neat dark suit and hat. If my mother had arrived in Philadelphia with an idea of what the man she would marry was going to be like, it probably did not resemble my father. I imagine my mother stared at him while he talked faster and faster, determined to fill the air between them with words, friendly words and tempting ones, until Lillian Jacobs finally said that yes, she would go to dinner with him.

And I imagine that, with just the slightest upward tilt of her eyes, she could look over my father's head, at the eagle whose wings were fused to its side, and feel again the sharp stab of disappointment that something wonderful was, in fact, not going to happen. My mother arrived in Philadelphia with some kind of plan for herself. With her refined sense of entitlement and a perhaps inflated estimate of her own potential, she probably believed that all you had to do to fly was stretch your wings, and let the wind raise you up. To gauge the wind, wait for it, ride the gusts and glide gracefully until the next one swept you up, was to be expected. She was prepared for that. It was, after all, how she had escaped Vermont.

But she never imagined that even the stretch could be denied. She never imagined wings that might not work. So she let him buy her a plate of chicken chow mein.

My parents started dating in April of 1939. By that summer, my father had proposed, and my mother accepted. At my mother's insistence, they planned a simple service in front of a Justice of the Peace in City Hall, a stone's throw from John Wanamaker's Department Store and the site of their first meeting. Irving would have preferred a religious ceremony, ideally back home in Brooklyn in front of friends and family. But he wanted more to make her happy; to give his betrothed what she wanted. It was the beginning of a pattern of behavior he would maintain until the day she left. But it couldn't keep her from leaving.

Sometime in their first year of marriage, the newly-weds did visit my mother's family in Vermont. This I know because there was a photo taken of my parents, looking impossibly young and standing on the porch of the white house in Vermont. So my mother did not return to Vermont with a college degree, or an exciting career, a reality that probably didn't even register for her family. Because she came back from Philadelphia with a husband. Certainly Lillian's husband did not compare to Jack Fein, but he was Jewish and college-educated, and Lillian—who was prickly and resisted domesticity or anything considered "wifely"—could have done much worse.

They honeymooned in Atlantic City. In pictures I have of them, they are posed stiffly on the boardwalk, formally dressed, both wearing hats, and my mother's fox stole makes its first appearance. It must have been part of her trousseau. They look nervous, and young, which they were: my mother barely twenty-one, my father almost twenty-four.

The fact of their marriage mystifies me as much today as it did throughout my childhood. They seem so ill-suited for one another.

They returned to Philadelphia, where my mother moved out of the Rittenhouse Square rooming house and into my father's tiny apartment on Chestnut Street above a shoe store. She continued to work at Wanamaker's, although I suspect she would rather not have. She was married now, and she had very precise ideas about what married ladies did; they shopped at Wanamaker's, they didn't work there. And they decorated. My mother felt keenly the absence of a home she could decorate, and her husband saw in those feelings an opportunity.

My father had been itching for quite some time to return to New York. He missed his sisters. He missed the Jewish delis on Flatbush Avenue. But what he missed most of all was a community: neighbors who knew him, a synagogue to belong to, even if he didn't want to attend services, friends and extended family to whom he could show off his pretty young wife. But while Lillian seemed to have no special affinity for Philadelphia, she had shown no interest at all in moving to New York.

So he bribed her. He promised her a two-bedroom apartment in a nice neighborhood. He promised her a decorating budget. He promised her she wouldn't have to work; he *insisted* on it, which was just the way my mother needed it to be expressed: *My husband insists that I not work.*

And he promised her that they would look at houses.

It was easy enough to arrange a transfer back to New York; he was not a senior enough member of the federal agency for which he worked to be valuable in any one place. And Lillian seemed to enjoy the apartment-hunting, in which she was joined by her new sisters-in-law, the freshness of the marriage keeping everyone on their best behavior. She found a sunny, two-bedroom apartment not far from Sadie and Thelma, which would please him, but far enough that they wouldn't be dropping in unannounced. Her husband, she thought, would have wanted to live *with* them if he could. Although she didn't particularly like Brooklyn, my mother liked her new status as a married matron and a woman of leisure.

She bought new furniture and drapes and bedroom sets for both rooms. She wallpapered, even though it was a rental. Her extravagance shocked her sisters, when they came to visit, and her sisters-in-law. But she didn't care, and neither did he. He could see it made her happy, and already, just months into her marriage, he was seeing glimpses of her black moods, her shapeless dissatisfaction that he couldn't seem to soothe. He began the reactive pattern that he would repeat for the next seventeen years of their marriage; when Lillian was angry or unhappy, her husband jumped into action: solving the problem, or at least hiding it; removing the offending item; bribing her with something he knew she wanted, for herself or for the house.

They moved into the new apartment on April Fool's Day, 1940, and after all her hard work, my mother seemed unhappy. She claimed to not be feeling well, and in fact she hadn't been feeling well for several days. She didn't help at all to unload the moving truck, just asked that her bed be reassembled right away so that she could lie down, and she was not seen for the rest of the day. My father was carrying boxes and helping the movers; he had had the foresight to have a telephone installed, and he was calling everyone he could think of to announce his return to Brooklyn; he even prepared sandwiches for dinner and invited Sadie and Thelma over to eat with him. And through it all, Lillian did not emerge from the bedroom.

Later that night, while my father was unpacking the china and looking carefully for chips and cracks (he found none), my mother got up out of bed and entered her new, brightly lit bathroom. She turned sideways to the full-length mirror and lifted her nightgown up over her hips, exposing the white cotton panties and the distinct bulge that began just below her breasts, which also looked bigger to her unpracticed eye. She had never before in her life looked with such attention at her naked body.

My mother sighed. She dropped her nightgown and adjusted it so that it hung evenly off her wide shoulders. She went to her room to retrieve a robe, which she put on before joining her husband in the kitchen to tell him she was pregnant.

CHAPTER THREE

I am sixty-five years old, an award-winning teacher recently retired from the New York City public schools. I have lived in the same apartment my entire adult life, in a large building on the corner of Sutton Place in Manhattan. I own it now. I don't smoke cigarettes, anymore. I don't drink alcohol. Anymore. I have been sober for sixteen years.

I have three sons. I have lost each of them, and found them, and now it seems that I have lost them again.

You are as sick as your secrets, they say in AA, and I am living proof of that. I have kept secrets my whole life; I lost my virginity against my will, and never spoke about it; I married a man I didn't love and pretended to be happy. I had a baby boy I was forced to give away for adoption and told everyone my husband's story that he had died at birth, and kept that secret for thirty-five years, until I couldn't anymore.

I have always done as I was told. I pursued the career my father told me I should. I married the kind of man my mother told me was appropriate. I gave away a baby my husband told me he could not love, and then never searched

51

for my lost son because my therapist told me it wasn't a good idea. The therapist told me that I would ruin his life if I found him because he may not even know that he was adopted. In fact, she emphasized that it could be a total disaster for him. I had a third son because my husband told me I owed him that, and then, when he left me and took my children with him, I didn't fight him for them. I had a psychiatrist who told me I'd be better off without my boys, who told me I'd never date or marry again if I fought to keep them and who scared me with terrifying scenarios: unsuccessful battles for child support, a life on welfare, and ultimately losing them anyway. And I had a lawyer who refused to plead my case on the advice of my psychiatrist. I was surrounded by people who spoke for me and decided for me and erased me. I was told to keep secrets, and I did. Until now.

My mother scolded me often for making noise, for speaking up and out. So I learned not to.

Shut up, you little brat. Stop making life difficult for me with your big mouth. Just shut up. Don't you get it? You really don't count, so don't waste your breath. I am not going to listen to you anyway, get it? If you don't get it, it's your tough luck. Listen to your mother: LITTLE GIRLS SHOULD BE SEEN AND NOT HEARD. Tell it to yourself if you must, but nobody else wants to hear from you. If you want to stay here, shut up! Go away, little girl. I will not love you if I hear one more word. Stop complaining!

But Mommy, I'm not complaining.

You're causing trouble. Keep quiet. Little girls should be seen and not heard.

∽

It was 1962. I was twenty-two years old, one year out of college, and I was living in Queens, New York. Ostensibly, I was living with my father and my sister Sandra, commuting by subway to classes at New York University to get my M.A. degree in Education. However, my father was never home during the week. His work usually required extensive travel outside of New York. When he came home for the weekend, he was out dancing at Roseland or with friends. Sandra was attending Oberlin College and living in the dormitory. So, basically, I was living alone.

The days and nights in that silent apartment were very troubling for me. I had grown up feeling disconnected from my parents and Sandra, my sister, who was three years younger. My mother excelled at managing her family, but not at nurturing it, and finally, in my junior year of high school, she left us, with no warning at all; just an empty apartment, missing cash and a note so unfeeling that nothing would have been preferable. I switched schools many times growing up, experiencing almost yearly the loneliness of the "new kid." My father's job kept him away; my mother's indifference kept me silent and obedient. So, although I finally seemed to have this home in Queens, there wasn't anyone around to love or nurture me.

I looked and acted okay, but I didn't really feel okay. I felt so fearful of having something bad happen while I was all alone, with nobody to help. It was lonely when I came home at night and nobody was there to eat dinner with. One weekend, I told my father how I felt.

"Daddy, I'm not happy," I told him. "I don't want to be all alone. Can I please get a roommate to live here with me?"

My father thought it was a good idea and allowed me to put an ad in *the New York Times* to look for a roommate. Ann lived with me, and when my father came home on the weekends, it felt like this was my family. But this arrangement had to change when Sandra came home from college in June. Then, Ann moved down the hall on the same floor, to share an apartment with another single woman.

For one year, I commuted to Manhattan to complete my MA in Education. My father had always wanted me to be a teacher. I had argued vehemently with him, telling him what a big waste of time those education courses seemed to be. Especially after taking one in my freshman year at Bennington, I just wasn't interested. I can still hear him telling me, and I think I always will hear him telling me: *If you are a teacher, you will always have something to fall back on. You will always be able to take care of yourself. Go back to school and take those courses; I'll pay for it.* So, after a hiatus of one year of trying out jobs in the advertising and publishing fields, I decided that the offer was a good one and I matriculated at NYU.

My father was right, although I wouldn't know it for a long time, wouldn't know that circumstances and bad choices would one day force me to have to take care of myself, and that my education would be the only tool I possessed for doing that.

In physical appearance, I was a five-six brunette with a really good figure and a pretty face. I had a perfectly shaped widow's peak and naturally arched thick dark eyebrows. I was always able to communicate well with my dark, deep-set eyes, although I had well learned how to cover up my real feelings. If I was upset, I could still have a smile on my face and a smile in my eyes. My teeth looked good enough due to the braces I needed to wear until I was thirteen years old. My mouth was on the small size with a "cupid-shaped" top lip.

I had one of those feminine builds with long, shapely legs; strong, full thighs and delicate ankles. I was not flat-chested, nor was I very buxom. I had small and firm breasts and a real small waist. My behind always stuck out. Although I was told that it was sexy, I always felt very conscious about this protrusion, and I usually made sure to wear clothes that would cover it up. I tried hard to detract from it by wearing a belt and a flared skirt to accentuate my waistline. I loved clothes, and I looked good in them if I bought the right color and a flattering style. I took a lot of pride in my appearance, and I always tried to be as well dressed as possible. I had picked this up in my senior year of high school when I attended a private boarding school in Connecticut.

I enjoyed putting myself together and making a good impression on other people. I think it was important to me because I felt insecure and unloved on the inside so I would have to impress people by how I looked and dressed on the outside.

I never liked my high-bridge, Roman and Jewish-looking nose. However, I did learn to accept it, since everyone told me it was okay just the way it was. I can remember that it wasn't the ski-slope style I had obsessed about in high school. My father even took me to our family doctor to discuss the pros and cons of having a nose job. That doctor was able to convince me that since there was nothing wrong with it, and that as long as I didn't have any trouble breathing, it was the nose God wanted me to have. So, I decided I would keep it.

Girls and young women never seem satisfied with the bodies God gives them, and I was definitely not satisfied with mine. I longed to be thinner. I usually weighed around 140 pounds, always wishing to be around 125 pounds. I had a real healthy appetite, and I never counted the calories. One of my favorite activities involved ice cream. My father called it a "walk and a talk." This dated back to my high

school days in Flatbush, when my father would take me to
Schrafft's on Flatbush Avenue near Church Avenue, and we
would get a double scoop of chocolate with almonds in a
sugar cone. We would walk and talk about a problem and
come to some kind of a reasonable solution or a decision.
This time we spent together was very meaningful to me
and made me feel loved.

I was an affectionate, physical, healthy girl, and as hard
as I tried, I couldn't make my body behave. I liked to kiss
and hug and hold hands. I liked to touch. There was very
little touching within my family, and as I entered adoles-
cence, this powerful conflict, this split between my mind
and my body, made interactions with the opposite sex
stressful. I am not alone in this, I know. So many women of
my generation struggled to protect their bodies from "viola-
tion" in order to maintain a good reputation. But this meant
denying themselves the pleasures of physical intimacy until
they were firmly established as wives, when, hopefully, it
would all fall into place, and the endless battles to protect
our chastity could be abandoned. Until, at eighteen, I began
my first serious relationship. Alex and I would be together
for almost two years, and as a result of his raping me, I
would experience the consequences of the mind/body split;
the terrible cost that my mother extracted from me, and
this culture has asked of girls.

I was never comfortable with men. On the outside, at
least, I was an unexceptional product of my time and place:
upper middle class, Jewish, New Yorker; 1950s American
teenage girl. I was pretty enough to attract boys, but that
was where it stopped. Like many, if not most, Jewish girls
of my generation, I was given the template of how a "nice
Jewish girl" looked and acted and was expected to conform
to that model: don't talk to strangers; don't ask questions
about things that shouldn't concern you, especially about

your body; sex is an obligation of marriage, never a source of pleasure; desire is reserved for men. The worst thing that could happen to a girl of my age and class would be to acquire a reputation as a "bad girl." I absorbed these rules and tried my hardest to live by them. My virginity would be reserved as a gift for my husband, whoever he turned out to be. I would allow "light petting" (above the waist), but only with a steady boyfriend, and never, never permit "heavy petting," which would "lead to other things," most notably pregnancy. My mother was a big prude, deeply uncomfortable with anything sexual, and was successful in getting me to distrust the opposite sex. She told me stories about child molesters—men who ruined young girls for life and left them broken and defiled with their panties stuffed in their mouths. She told me, in all seriousness, that babies were delivered by the stork. When I was twelve and a "boyfriend" tried to kiss me, I slapped him with the full force of my mother's puritanical outrage.

It was inevitable that I would be a "daddy's girl," and ironic too, since my mother caused both that special bond between my father and me, by withholding her affection, and then resentment. As parents, they defined the term "polar opposites." Where she was critical, he was encouraging; where she was cool and reserved, he was warm and effusive. Part of this was his attempt, sweet but ultimately futile, to compensate for her lack of interest in his girls. But a mother's love can't be replaced. It's absence will always wound, no matter how loving a father a child has.

I think my father knew this. I think he showered Sandra and me with affection and attention to try and reduce the severity of the inevitable wound. And I am grateful.

CHAPTER FOUR

My father always liked to play sports, but not to watch them. He liked to eat, but not to cook—not that he ever had a chance. His two sisters, Sadie and Thelma, never let him do for himself if they could help it, and my mother refused him access to the kitchen for fear he'd make a mess, which could result in more work for herself. He loves the sun, and most summer afternoons will find him relaxing on a bench in Prospect Park. For years he was a member of the Landover Beach Club in Rockaway Beach, where he was known as the Mayor. He knew every single member, their children and grandchildren and their preferred cocktail. He knew who liked sun and who liked shade, and would arrange the chaise lounges accordingly. He would stroll around the pool, greeting other members with kisses or firm handshakes and offer to get anything they might need: towel, reading material, cold drink or snack. He was much loved at the Landover Beach Club, and even though he no longer feels up to the trip out to Rockaway on a regular basis, he still goes out two or three times over the course of the summer. He tries to pay a guest fee when he gets there, and is told, every time, that his money's no good. *Hey!* people will call out as he strolls—a little less energetically now; he is, after all, eighty-nine—his first time around the pool. *Hey! It's the Mayor!*

But by far, the thing my father loves the most, after his family, is music. He has music everywhere he is: the car radio is tuned to the Latin station, and he and Thelma regularly play records. He likes the crooners of the forties, fifties and sixties: Sinatra, Tony Bennett, Bobby Darin, Connie Francis and Peggy Lee. Rosemary Clooney. He likes Liza. He likes Nora Jones. He loves to dance, although he no longer spends his weekends at the Roseland Ballroom. But he dances around Thelma's cluttered living room. And he hums. All the time.

As a child, my father was the one who put Sandra and me to bed, and he would always sing a lullaby for each of us. Sandra liked funny, lively songs like "Pack Up Your Troubles" and "If You Knew Susie," and he would sometimes personalize the lyrics, such as changing "Susie" to "Sandy," after which he would whisper devilishly: *Don't tell your mother.* We were forbidden to call Sandra by anything but her proper name.

For me, he always sang sweet and comforting songs—"Lullaby and Goodnight" and "I Love You Truly"— and I would immediately feel my body relax. I was an anxious and confused child, and I needed my father's song, this declaration of love delivered in his deep, melodious singing voice, before I could feel safe enough to sleep. In the morning, when I woke to a new day of my mother's moods and demands, and a life that always felt somehow tenuous, I would replay my lullaby to remind me of my one true thing—my father's love.

I think he is happy with Thelma, and she with him. She won't let him smoke in the house, and although he grumbles and complains about it, he complies, which means he has to cut down on his ever-present Chesterfields, and that's a good thing. She cooks his favorite foods and does his laundry, and sometimes at night they sink their heavy, stiff bodies into the fat cushions of Thelma's floral- patterned sofa and watch TV in companionable silence. I feel very comforted to know that they are together. My father is a man who needs a woman to take care of him; she is a woman who needs to take care of a man. He retired nine years ago, and I think he still misses it. In the end, sales was a good choice for him. He has the gift of gab, and his good nature has always inspired trust.

His health is always a concern. His heart isn't strong. It never has been. He had rheumatic fever as a child and has been a heavy smoker most of his life. Each burden he was forced to carry—my mother's abrupt departure, the stress of being the sole breadwinner—seemed to affect his health until finally, at age fifty-five, he had open heart surgery. He had one of the very first experimental aorta valve replace-ments. The surgeon even showed me what it looks like. Now, more than thirty years later, his arteries are clogged, his valves are sluggish, his beat irregular. But the condition of the *muscle* has little relation to the state of my father's heart, if heart is the place where a man stores his capacity to love and forgive and accept and give. He gives his heart freely to his cantankerous sisters and often lost daughters; his heart, he'll say, belongs to his grandchildren, even the grandson he has yet to meet. My father's heart is great and full.

You could definitely call my father a sport. When I was in middle school and we lived on Long Island, he was the one who took a car full of girls every year to Coney Island for the day to celebrate my birthday. He took us to Steeple-chase and everyone got a card, which was punched as we went from one ride to the next, for at least ten different rides.

At the entrance, everyone had to walk or crawl through a big barrel that turned to the tune of "Roll Out the Barrel."

After we finished all the rides and ate a real lunch, there were so many more treats we would stuff ourselves with. My friends and I would wander along the boardwalk in twos and threes, my father always keeping an eye on everyone. As we wandered along the main drag, at every food or game counter, he would offer its delights.

"Who wants to play this?" he'd ask. "Who's hungry?" We always had franks, French fries and deep fried fantail shrimp at Nathan's, frozen custard ice cream cones, and cotton candy; one after the next as we continued our stroll. There were so many games to play as we made our way to the beginning of Coney Island, to the rollercoaster. We passed the Greyhound races, skeeball, Tirza the Wine Bath girl marinating her smooth white body in a tub of red wine—my father loved her, but could never stop himself from some wisecrack about the vintage. *Ach!* he'd say, *forty-seven, not a good year for Lambrusco. She'll taste like vinegar,* he'd say, nodding toward Tirza and cackling.

He'd go with us on the scary Hall of Horrors ride with skeletons popping out of the wall forcing you to hold your breath, about to hit you in the face, when the motorized car pulled away just in time to save you, daylight hitting you when the ride was over, and we returned to reality. But the scariest ride was also the very last: the famous Coney Island Cyclone. My friends and I would get quieter and quieter as we got closer to it. We were terrified of it, but no one ever refused the ticket my father handed to each of us. We were safely secured into our seats and went slowly up, up, up, and then down, down, so fast that I practically stopped breathing. We screamed like banshees.

At the end of the day, everyone went home exhausted. Satiated with fun and food. It was when their parents called later that evening complaining that their daughters were sick to their stomachs and throwing up that I knew they really had a wonderful time. Of course, they all wanted to be my friends so they would be invited to my birthday party the next year.

My father always bought extra tickets so I could invite friends for any event he was planning to take us to. Whether it was the Ballet Russe de Monte Carlo, the Ringling Brothers Barnum & Bailey circus, or a Broadway show, there usually were extra tickets and a requirement to invite friends. Even once when he chartered a cruise boat, with a crew, I was told to invite a couple of friends to come along with us. But my mother never approved of my friends, and objected to the money "wasted" on frivolities. Consequently, these excursions that my father led like a benevolent but slightly over- caffeinated tour guide, had an air of intrigue and sneakiness to them, which made me love them more. *Don't tell your mother*, he would whisper. *Don't tell your mother.*

He was the one I cried to when I didn't want to leave the car on those dreadful days—any day with even a hint of a cloud in the sky—when my mother thought it might rain. My father would drive me to school, looking like a rubber banana on the seat next to him, dressed head to toe in bright yellow rain gear and choking back sobs. My mother would send me to school overdressed with high yellow rain boots over my calves, a yellow rain coat down to my knees and a wool hat with earflaps. And of course, an umbrella. Oh, how much I loved my father when he told me I could take that all off, leave it in the car, thereby sparing me the humiliation of entering my school like a fluorescent yellow testimonial to my mother's obsessiveness and lack of empathy. My father would make me promise never to tell Mommy—which I never did—but I always remember.

I remember his compassion and his ability to "get" how I felt; I remember the look in his eyes, how he knew what it felt like to walk in my shoes, or, more accurately, my yellow rubber boots.

One of the great tragedies of my father's life was that he was a father and a husband, but could never be both at the same time. Surrounded by needy females who wanted attention from him and had little commerce with each other, he ran interference: between Sandra and me—certainly our sibling rivalry probably ran a little deeper than most—but more dramatically, between my mother and her daughters. He protected her, as much as he could, from the children she bore, but wasn't able to raise. He knew how shallow was the well of his wife's maternal instinct. He tried to compensate. He tried to give us more because his wife couldn't give us very much.

And he protected us from her; from her hypercritical eye and sharp tongue, from the eccentricities she was never content to indulge on her own. She saw us as an extension of herself, rather like the extension leaves of the cherry dining room table we had in Roslyn. Sometimes she wanted that table expanded to its full length; sometimes, when we were entertaining, it needed to be. But more often she wanted more space in the room, less table to clean and protect from scratches and spills and fingerprints. Mostly she kept her table reduced to its smallest, least expansive alternative shape and size —a card table-sized square—while the leaves gathered dust in the hall closet.

When our mother noticed us at all, it was usually to "improve" us, which generally meant criticizing us, or forcing us to adhere to whatever crazy rule or prohibition was on her mind that day: *You must sleep in flannel pajamas after October 15,* or *You must block the transom of your bedroom door to prevent drafts of cold air that could make you sick*. Anything but that! My mother dreaded above all else having to care for us.

But when Daddy looked at his girls, he saw not inconvenience, chaos, rebelliousness; he saw the future, he saw potential and creativity and the capacity for joy; he saw love—the love we had for him, and him for us. How hard it must have been for him, balanced on that thin, blurry line between wife and children. Nothing could have prepared him for what my mother demanded, subtly through most of their marriage, and overtly when she left him: that he choose.

So he tried, and tried harder, to avoid that choice. He tried to keep all of us happy, tried to make sure each one of the three of us knew we were loved, tried to prevent conflict by inserting himself between warring camps. *Did you listen to your mother?* he'd ask us every evening when he came home from work. Not only to remind us that we should, but also to prepare himself for the mood he would find my mother in; a bad report from us or a host of complaints about how she had mistreated us, and he would expect her blackest mood and most extreme demands. It was during those moods that my mother would begin to campaign for boarding schools. The seeds of those terrible years living away from my family were planted on days when I'd failed to listen to my mother.

The charts on the side of the attic steps were another attempt to mediate household harmony. My father was a very organized, action-oriented man, and it would seem that the charts were his idea. But I don't think they were. I think they were my mother's idea; a way to enforce her standards for our environment and behavior without actually dealing with us directly. There is something about a chart listing twenty-five tasks—from the mundane (tooth-brushing) to the annoying (piano practice) to the redundant (take a bath)—which seems right in line with my mother's approach to parenting: if it's all on a chart, you'll never have to talk to them.

But it was my father, of course, who had to monitor those charts, a role he assumed with some embarrassment. Still, if it would keep peace in his household, he'd do it. He tried to make light of the humiliation when he had to ask Sandra and me to check off on the chart that we'd bathed when it was obvious we had. We'd roll our eyes or flush with embarrassment, and he'd start to read down the list in a silly, singsong voice, adding and subtracting as he went along—*Did you catch a bee? Did you lose your key? Did you drink your tea? Did you take a pee?*—until finally we would laugh, and he could relax; disaster, catastrophe, chasms and landslides avoided for one more day. For one more day, maybe, we could all get along.

That's really all my father ever wanted: that the people he loved could love each other.

Can I get you anything? My father still says that, all the time—to his friends at the coffee shop, to the cleaning woman Thelma has finally agreed to employ every other week, to the doormen outside the large apartment buildings on Flatbush Avenue as he passes them on the way to the newsstand, to me when I come to visit. *Can I get you anything?* And he really wants to. He is a rare breed, my father. The source of his happiness is the happiness of others.

"Daddy," I said the last time I saw him, "they should bottle you." He threw back his head and laughed, red-cheeked and twinkle-eyed, his hand straying automatically to pat the full head of thick wavy hair he's managed to hold on to. He looked like a leprechaun. "You look like a Jewish leprechaun," I said.

"*Oy vey,*" he said, and laughed harder.

On the corner of Ludlow and Rivington, where my father was born and lived his first ten years, there's a bar now, called Motor City. There's a pet boutique, a fancy sandwich shop specializing in panini, New York's hip food of the hour. And there's a diner run by Dominicans, which serves Spanish food and has become unaccountably trendy despite its shabbiness, and so has survived the gentrification that has erased any trace of the Lower East Side my father knew. Once Sandra had the idea that we should take our father there on an outing, spend the day with him exploring his old neighborhood, go out to lunch, see how things have changed. But Dad wasn't interested.

"Why would I want to go there?" he asked. "It was a place people left."

One of the few things my parents had in common was their status as the children of Russian Jews; hardworking immigrants who left the turmoil in Eastern Europe and sprinkled themselves, ever hopeful, throughout this land. But while my mother's people settled in small, clean Bennington, nestled under the protective arms of the Green Mountains and surrounded by other immigrants, also Jewish and mostly Russian, my father's family, headed by his father, the chain-smoking, pinochle-playing grandfather I barely remember, took only baby steps away from Ellis Island, to Manhattan's Lower East Side.

The Lower East Side, a crisscross of narrow streets lined with tenements—sandwiched between the East River and Broadway; south of Houston, north of Canal—harbored an international mix of residents which, in that historical moment, was unduplicated anywhere else on the planet. Anchored by the burgeoning Chinese population and their rapidly expanding Chinatown, and the clannish Italians with their social clubs and cafes, the neighborhood attracted immigrants of all other flavors who filled the small dark apartments in the tenements as well as the manufacturing jobs available in the industrial buildings of present day SoHo. It wasn't a melting pot; more like an uneasy salad, diversity before we knew to value it.

But I think it explains something about my father, a man described by everyone as "easygoing"; I think his childhood, thrown together as he was with so many Others, exposed by close quarters to so much Difference, shaped his world view, making him the generous and accepting man I have always known him to be. He is "non-judgmental" embodied.

"Ach," he would say. "Life's too short. Let 'em be who they are."

So my father's parents, Bernard and his wife, settled on Ludlow Street, in a five-floor walk-up bursting at the seams with immigrant families. The young couple soon had a daughter, and then another, and then my father, the son for whom they anxiously awaited. Sadly, Fannie didn't have much time to enjoy her children. When my father was four, she caught a cold that worsened into untreated pneumonia, and Fannie died so quickly that it left her family in shock. My father's memories of his mother are hazy and romanticized, it has always seemed to me. When he would speak of Fannie, he always evoked a woman of uncommon beauty and goodness, an angel who transformed their shabby three-room apartment into a home of warmth and abundance; an unwavering source of love. His stories were rarely confirmed by Sadie or Thelma, who seldom spoke of their mother, and whose grief, as daughters and older children at the time of her death was probably sharper and more lasting. But I don't think anyone begrudged my father his sentimental memories of the mother he barely knew, regardless of their questionable veracity. His tendency to see the best in any person was a mark of his character, and everyone who knew him, even as a boy, basked in his optimism.

For high school, he returned to the Lower East Side, commuting to Seward Park High School, one of the city's better public secondary schools. Bernard didn't understand why his son would want to go back to the place he had worked so hard to take them away from. But by that time my father was thinking about his future; he was thinking about Sadie and Thelma, both still unmarried, although Thelma eventually would find a husband, and he was committed to their support. His sisters would never want for anything, he told himself; he would make sure of that. Education was the key, and he was going to college.

The war nearly derailed that plan, but his poor eyesight kept him out of the army and so, fitted with thick-lensed, wire-framed glasses and a somber expression befitting the seriousness with which he regarded higher education, he enrolled in City College, which was tuition-free to residents at the time. In a hurry to begin making money, he graduated in just three years with an accounting degree, and passed the CPA exam soon after. Focused on his studies, his future and his family, he did not date in college.

The job my father landed, at just twenty-one years old, impressed everyone, not least of all the boy with thinning hair and an impish grin who had to look, dressed in his first business suits, a little like a kid playing dress up. He had gotten a job as an auditor—a *government job!* Bernard would say reverently, with the immigrant's internalized respect for his adopted land, for a federal agency charged with oversight and enforcement of banking regulations. It was a good job—respectable and secure—with a good salary and regular raises. It was the kind of job a man kept for life.

When I think of that fresh-faced young man, feeling slightly awkward in the unfamiliar suit and tie, the empty briefcase dangling expectantly from his right hand as he left the undemanding warmth of his family and home to make his way in the world, I imagine he was nervous but certain; he came from people who loved and believed in him; his course was clear, and so far he had adhered to it without any swerves, bumps or particular difficulties. But oh how young we are at twenty-one! He didn't know about falling in love; of course he didn't. No one does until it happens.

At his interview, the man who would be my father's supervisor at the banking commission proudly listed the benefits of the job: the prestige and regular raises; the paid vacation and "opportunity to travel." My father didn't say anything at the time, but "opportunity to travel" was not a benefit in his eyes. He liked to be home. His father was aging, and he liked to stay close. His sisters provided for him so completely and loved him so unconditionally that any travel felt like a deprivation. Still, when after barely a year on the job his boss called him in and told him that he was being transferred to Philadelphia, where the commission was opening an office, my father was stoic. Although his boss presented this as a great opportunity for a younger employee, my father suspected he was being tapped for this transfer largely because he was unmarried and could relocate with less difficulty. He never considered refusing the transfer—he was a reliable and compliant employee— but the situation probably got him thinking about the next phase of his life's plan. He needed to marry. He had love to give, he knew this, and if by finding a recipient for all of his affection he also might insulate himself from similar disruptions in the future. . . . well then, that's what he would do. It made sense.

So that was the young man who arrived in Philadelphia. It was his first time away from home and he was lonely, and this loneliness probably increased his preoccupation with finding a wife. The "gentleman's efficiency" apartment that the commission had rented for him depressed him, and he took to spending as much time away from it as possible. At home, his sisters had never let him near the kitchen, and after one quick perusal of the mini-kitchen in his apartment, he began taking all his meals out. After a day at the office, he would have roast chicken or a thick pastrami sandwich at one of several diners he liked to frequent for their good food and pretty waitresses. After dinner he walked the city, sometimes stopping for a shave, haircut and shoeshine, other times calling home from a pay phone and assuring Sadie and Thelma that he was fine, warm enough and eating well. He wandered in and out of stores, occasionally buying something he needed, or a little something to send his sisters, and one of the stores he frequently visited was John Wanamaker's. Like his future wife, he had been told of the impressiveness of the bronze eagle, and the pipe organ on which a classically trained musician played two concerts a day, six days a week. He loved music, and the evening performance, which began at five forty-five p.m. and lasted until six-thirty p.m., often drew him to the atrium, where, of course, he met Lillian. She was a bit standoffish at first, which sparked his usually latent competitive streak. He thought she was different from any other woman he'd known, but he hadn't known very many women except his sisters. He thought she had class, and if my father had any insecurity, it sprang from his immigrant, Lower East Side, free university education background. He believed he lacked class. He thought Lillian was perfect for him. He thought she was a prize.

They lived in Irving's tiny little apartment, and both returned to work. *It's just temporary*, my father assured his new wife, referring to both the apartment and her job, leaving the promise intentionally vague. He knew he wanted to give his bride a more luxurious, a *classier* home. But he did not intend this home to be in Philadelphia. And by Valentine's Day, Lillian was pregnant.

Perhaps it was the pregnancy that sparked uncharacteristic vulnerability in my mother. Perhaps she did not want to be alone with a baby in a city where neither she nor her husband had family. Perhaps Brooklyn seemed the lesser of two evils, since she knew she did not want to go back to Vermont. Whatever it was that eroded my mother's defenses, my father got his wish within months of the wedding; he convinced his wife to return with him to Brooklyn, and when he put in for a transfer at the banking commission, he found to his delight that, as a married man, his request was granted immediately. Undoubtedly there was another boy, just out of college and smooth-cheeked, in an ill-fitting suit with an empty briefcase, who could be sent to Philadelphia to take my father's place. And my father, with his pregnant wife on his arm and his own briefcase no longer empty, but bulging with the documents and spreadsheets of an important man with an important job, came home to Brooklyn.

It is here where my father's story begins to swerve off of that clean, straight, well-lit corridor. It is here where his path twists in unexpected and unwelcome ways, and where the inherent optimism that had served him well up until this point becomes inadequate. What he needed, perhaps, was knowledge: about marriage—without even two parents to observe, he had no direct experience of the bond; and about women—yes, he knew his sisters well, but they in no way prepared him for the mercurial and ambitious woman he now called his wife, his prize. But sometimes a prize is not a blessing.

His mistake, he would think later, was in trying to satisfy a woman who could not be satisfied; not by the sunny, two-bedroom apartment in Borough Park, which was not a house and not in the suburbs, and so would forever irritate rather than gratify his wife. She could not be satisfied, either (and this was a bitter pill for him to swallow) by the dream baby she delivered the following October. To his eyes, little Myrna was perfect; the most beautiful baby who ever existed in the world, matched in intelligence and loveliness only by her sister Sandra, who joined them three years later. He loved being a father and, encouraged both by circumstances and his own desire, he took an active role in the raising of his babies, compensating for his wife's reserve, her *indifference* even, although he would never, could never have used that word. What he knew was that Lillian seemed to lack some fundamental supply of patience and affection, qualities his sisters had had in abundance. But having never known his mother, he couldn't really say what a mother's love was supposed to look like, and he was too kind a man to give voice to what he feared: that Lillian didn't love their daughters. Sometimes the thought crept in despite his attempts to avoid it, for instance, when one of the girls would cry and his wife would continue whatever she was doing without pause, as if she didn't even hear it. And he would think to himself what he had always heard: that mothers were especially tuned to the cries of their children, that the compelling need to respond to those cries was in a mother's DNA. Not Lillian. And sometimes, when she would thrust one of the girls at him and snap *Take her!* he could see what a burden it was to his wife to care for them. He could see it in the tense way she held her shoulders whenever Myrna or Sandra did something to displease her, which was often. He could hear it in the long, deep sigh from her side of their bed, in the mornings when the first sounds of giggling or little running feet drifted to them from their daughters' bedroom, and his wife prepared to confront another day.

He did not blame her. He didn't believe it was something she could help. He didn't think she knew it was going to be this way. It was some kind of sickness, was how he thought of his wife's lack of maternal instincts, and you couldn't be angry at someone for being sick, could you? And then there was the jealousy, which was so far outside of how he imagined a family to be that he couldn't even admit it out loud: his wife was jealous of his daughters. She wanted to be the only girl in his life. Sometimes he wondered if things would have been better if they had had sons. But he knew there was no point to such mental meanderings. They didn't have sons, and he wouldn't trade his precious little girls for a million dollars or a million sons. Once, he had delicately brought up with his wife the possibility of one more baby—*Maybe they could have that boy*, he said, *maybe. . . .* He didn't complete the thought, but what he was thinking was *Maybe you could be a better mother to a son.* But it didn't matter. She told him in no uncertain terms that she was done with pregnancy, done with getting fat and having to work so hard to lose the weight, done with the smell and the noise of an infant in the house. The girls were finally in school; finally she could get some peace, especially now that Myrna was away at boarding school. No, Lillian was done having children, and to insure this, she limited him to once or twice a month, during times when her cycle told her it was safe.

His wife was a complainer, and he was her target and her audience. He just wanted everyone to be happy. That was how he saw his role: the mediator, the fixer, the gofer. He tried to give his family everything they wanted, and when they still weren't happy—the girls whined and misbehaved and irritated their mother; Lillian yelled and snapped and retreated to her bedroom for hours at a time—he tried harder. Sometimes on weekends, when the girls were busy with their friends and Lillian was lying down, he would take the subway to Coney Island and walk along the beach, thinking it all over, trying to figure out exactly what was wrong with his family, and how to make it better.

And that was how it started.

Lillian wanted a house. She had grown up in a house, and felt that living in an apartment was beneath her. It was a step backwards; she did not marry to have *less* than she started with, was how she put it to Irving, every time she spoke to him about it, which was every day. At first he reminded her that he was still a junior man at the banking commission, but there was every expectation that, with the regular promotions he was sure to get, and the automatic raises that a government job guaranteed, eventually they would be able to move. All the senior auditors lived in houses in the suburbs, he told his wife. It was just a matter of time. That's how it worked.

But his wife stopped listening at "junior man," which somehow confirmed her opinion of her husband. He *was* "junior;" ineffective, a less than adequate provider; less than a man. She didn't have to say these hurtful things; Irving knew how she felt, and rather than getting angry—he hadn't come from angry people; he didn't know the ways that some people converted hurt to rage—he turned his attention toward proving her wrong.

Whatever was the proverbial straw that broke the camel's back, I can't say. From what I remember, the end came quickly. There was one night when my father didn't come home for dinner, and my mother had the maid feed us in the kitchen while she stayed in her room. Later, we could hear the shrill tone of her voice, but not what she was saying. Something about, as my mother so delicately put it, my father's "reversal of fortune."

She had been a mother in name only. Now, she was a wife in name only as well.

CHAPTER FIVE

Eli Kramer looks like the kind of work he does. An Ivy League educated lawyer, he dresses in a typical style, indistinguishable from other lawyers his age and status, except that his clothes are usually rumpled. If you searched his pockets, you would find unmailed, unpaid bills mixed with small pieces of paper with scribbled notes. Even his full head of silver-white hair never really looks combed. On weekdays, he wears a conservative shirt, suit and tie with black oxford shoes and black socks. Most of his ties are nondescript, not like the bright splashes of color we see on Ivy League lawyers today. His air of distinction does not come from a polished and put-together look. It comes from his thick hair and substantial body, which seems to broadcast affluence and confidence, an attitude he has the ability to maintain even when he is or should be neither. Eli has always *looked* like a mature and knowledgeable lawyer.

When Eli is pondering an idea, he usually puts a finger in his mouth. You knew that he was about to make a decision as the deep furrows on his forehead got deeper and he made a grimace. Eli lets you know what he thinks and why, based on his law school background or his interpretation of the facts. His gruff voice tells you that he has the definitive answer and that he is absolutely right. One should not bother to argue or try to dissuade him from his decision. He's got the right answer and he knows it all.

Eli Kramer is about five-eight, and his prematurely gray hair has always made him look older than his actual age. His body type also makes him look older. He has narrow shoulders and a belly, usually hidden by a dark suit or a blue blazer. To this day, as he walks with his stocky build and his left-handed and left footed stride and full head of hair, he carries the air of a senator or an important public personality.

Both in bed and out of bed, Eli is sedentary. "Never sit up when you can lie down" is his favorite saying. Actually, he is always sitting or lying down. He stands only when necessary. Eli never really participates in sports and is not much of a physical person. Indeed, we didn't really dance together until our wedding when it was necessary. In fact, we even made an appointment to take a dancing lesson together in preparation for the big event. Eli never kept that appointment. I can't remember any special kind of music that Eli liked or even disliked.

My husband loved sports and watched as many ballgames as possible. Name the season and the popular sport, and he was watching it. His diversion was to keep his own score in pencil. The TV was always on loud with some sporting event blasting in the background. This bothered me because I really wasn't interested in the games. I liked basketball and baseball and golf, but I didn't need the loud background noise or all the details.

Eli's father was in the meat business. As a result of too much meat in his house while he was growing up, Eli did not like any kind of red meat except for chopped beef. He would only eat hamburgers or meat loaf. And the only other dish he liked was tuna fish, especially warmed-up tuna with peas. With these preferences, I found it difficult to have very much variety in our dinner menus. The paradox was that on the exterior, Eli liked to impress himself and his friends by pretending to be a French gourmet. Although we never ate like that at home, Eli made it his business to try to go to all the fancy French restaurants so he could impress his friends when they came to our house for dinner. He read the reviews in Zagat and the newspapers and would repeat them to others, as if they were his own personal insights. I remember once hearing Eli tell some friends about the importance of the consistency in chocolate mousse and his personal recommendation, which came straight from the newspaper review for a restaurant where the consistency was perfect.

How can I describe Eli? He is a paradox. He exudes an air of confidence and bravado that does not exist when you really get to know him. Superficial bluster with no depth, that's Eli. I soon learned that you cannot believe a word he says. Eli loved poker and was very proud of his ability to bluff. He would describe how, with only one good card in his hand, he was able to bluff and fool his opponents. He could play act and keep his face blank, the original "poker face," so that other players thought he had good cards and would fold. Had I known to look for it, I could have gathered a lot of information about the character of the man I was married to for ten years by looking carefully at the way he played poker.

Eli played in a weekly game for large stakes but I never knew whom or where he played. His regular monthly poker game with his friends alternated. When it was our turn, I was not allowed to come out of my room or be the "hostess with the mostest." I just had to make sure that special staples were available: munchies, cheesecake and cream, milk and coffee.

I know Eli was very proud of this ability to bluff, and it extended beyond poker. He seemed to have a hard time "playing by the rules." He did not keep promises. I remember one night Eli came home and he was very despondent. I asked him what was wrong. He told me he couldn't tell me but that it had to do with money. I told him that if he told me what the problem was, I would help him by giving him my three-and-a-half carat diamond engagement ring. He said he had to think about it, and he would take a walk around the block. He soon returned and we sat at the dining room table while Eli told me about cash flow problems at his law firm—some expected money that hadn't come in, and some unplanned expenses. We never talked about money, and I was surprised and moved that he felt he could confide in me. I offered my ring again, and he promised that he would just put it in hock and that I would definitely get it back within the year. I agreed.

Years later, when Eli promised to take me on a trip to South America if I quit smoking for one full year, I was crushed but not really surprised when, after I endured the torment of detoxing from more than forty cigarettes a day, he told me he did not have the time or money to take our trip.

I went without him.

Eli was not an emotional person on the outside, and I never really got to know the inside. He rarely shared his daytime activities with me and he didn't complain about much either. I guess you might call him a nondescript or neuter personality. His job is to do the best for his clients, regardless of guilt or innocence.

Eli's family came from Brooklyn Heights. I never met his mother, because she had passed away before I knew him. However, they did keep a kosher home and considered themselves orthodox. His father, Fred, was a butcher and made a lot of money during World War II in the black market meat business. He insisted on paying for our Saturday night formal wedding, held at the Brooklyn temple where Fred was president. Fred was all of five feet tall, but he didn't act as if he knew it.

I liked Eli's family well enough, but had I looked more carefully at their relationships, the competition between them and the way Fred used both his money and his approval to manipulate his children, I probably would have understood my husband better. Fred truly believed that a person's value was determined by the amount of money he had. Fred considered himself a very valuable man, and he communicated to his family his satisfaction or disappointment with them by the size of his monetary gifts, which, when bestowed, were never as large as he had led them to expect. When I think about Eli now, I can see how his perpetual money problems, which he never admitted but rather ignored, were probably directly connected to his belief, instilled by Fred, that he must be affluent in order to be valuable. We never were affluent, really. It was another one of Eli's bluffs.

I did not find Eli to be communicative. Although we shared a bed, we each slept separate and apart in twin beds, both attached to the same king-sized headboard. He stayed on his side, and I stayed on mine. He got up early. I went to bed late. He fell asleep either writing in his work diary or watching TV and I stayed up late watching *the Late Show*, *the Late, Late Show* and sometimes even *the Late, Late, Late Show*. I was frustrated and lonely, and I had trouble falling asleep.

Our relationship was almost nonexistent. Our discussions were perfunctory, pertaining mostly to making plans to go out with another couple once a week, visiting with his family on Sundays, and the unpaid bills. We did not have any sex life together.

Because Eli didn't seem to really want to have sex, I was turned off as well. At one point, I asked him to please get a checkup to make sure that nothing was physically wrong with him. Perhaps if the problem was organic, it would explain his lack of desire. He went for the checkup, and everything was normal. Everything, that is, except our sex life. Eli was thirty-two when we married, but completely sexually inexperienced.

Eli has been living with the same woman, Gracie, for more than twenty years now, on Madison Avenue in midtown. I've heard that they sleep in separate bedrooms, but what they have in common is the allure of going to all the French restaurants on Madison Avenue, and a love of theatre. This lifestyle of shared interests seems to work for both of them. Gracie owns the co-op they live in and pays all the bills.

I don't believe Eli Kramer has ever faced himself squarely in the mirror. I don't believe he has ever admitted why he married me: because I was pretty, and Jewish—I pleased his family and looked good on his arm; because all his friends were married or getting married; because I was fun to be with, good company, and a good accessory; maybe, even, Eli married me because he was lonely. But I am certain he did not marry me because he loved me.

I didn't love him either.

In 1963, when I married Eli Kramer, I was lonely, immature and frightened. It didn't seem to matter that I didn't love Eli. In fact, it was probably a good thing. Not loving him felt safe, protection against being hurt. So I married him.

It all began with a blind date.

In the fall of the year I started my courses at NYU, a girlfriend Anne, who was dating a guy named Sam, wanted to fix me up on a blind date with Sam's roommate. His name was Eli. One night, Eli Kramer called me on the telephone and asked me out. I really didn't have any other social life, so I accepted.

The buzzer from the lobby rang loudly and, as I rushed to the hall to ring back, I felt suddenly frantic. He was early. I wasn't ready yet. I scurried to put on the black fabric flats I planned to wear to the front door. The pretty new white blouse, black cinch belt and floral flare skirt showed off my figure, and I was pleased with my appearance. Such excitement over a blind date!

I had been obsessing about Eli Kramer's height since his phone call the previous Monday, and I replayed our conversation as I waited for him to make his way up from the lobby.

"How tall are you?" I had asked him very directly. Height was a big deal for me.

"Why do you need to know?" he responded. "Is it important?"

"Well—yes," I said, figuring I might as well be honest. "I never go out with any man who isn't at least six feet tall." This was true. I was five-six, and I liked to feel smaller next to a taller guy. Somehow, it made me feel protected and less vulnerable. I felt safe with a tall man.

"Do you mean," Eli continued, sounding like a lawyer cross-examining a witness,

"that if I was five-eleven and a half, you wouldn't go out with me?" He made me sound shallow, and I suddenly felt foolish. I was glad we were on the phone.

"Of course I would," I said uncomfortably. I had just been lawyered, although I didn't realize it at the time. By agreeing that half an inch wasn't really *that* important, I had somehow just agreed to go out with Eli Kramer. Still, I didn't let it go.

"So, how tall **are** you?" I asked again, and Eli, the consummate litigator, admitted he wasn't five-eleven and a half. He was closer, he said, to five-eight and a half without shoes. Therefore, he would be about five-nine to five-ten with shoes. The exactness of his answer was dizzying, but reassuring. I could live with five-ten, I thought, but I still wanted to wear my flats first, to the door, before I chose a pair of heels for the evening. I had a choice of low, medium or very high heels. It was, as I said, a big deal for me.

The front doorbell interrupted my thoughts as I took a last glance in my bedroom mirror and walked quickly to the door.

"Who is it?" I called, as sweetly as possible.

"It's Eli." He had a strong, loud, clipped voice.

I didn't look through the peephole. I just turned the handle and opened the door wide. Based on our phone conversation, and what my girlfriend had told me, I had expected Eli to be an average, but attractive guy, eight years older, which would make him around thirty years old. But I hadn't really thought beyond that. I hadn't even realized how invested I was in a physical "type." All I knew was that there was a certain kind of man I found attractive, and when I opened the door to greet my future husband for the first time, my immediate thought was: *This man is not my type.*

Eli was shorter than I had pictured, and bulkier. His gray hair aged him beyond his thirty-one years, and I thought we would look odd together. I felt so disappointed, but I tried my best not to show it. I didn't want to hurt his feelings, so I composed my face and tried to welcome him gracefully.

"Please come in," I said, as I held the door open. "I'm Myrna." Eli extended his hand, smiled and said "Hello" in a very pleasant manner.

As he stepped over the marble threshold of our front door, I took in his small-sized shoe. And he was not five feet, ten inches tall. Not even close. He was more like five feet, eight inches, in his shoes. The fact that he would lie about something concrete and verifiable troubled me. But he seemed so much more mature than me, so much more reasonable. Maybe I was *un*reasonable to care about height, I thought, although what I really cared about was honesty, and I didn't feel I could call this mature, well-educated lawyer honest. So I resigned myself to spending the whole evening in flats, and shut the front door.

We walked into the living room. Eli smiled politely and asked me if there was a nice restaurant in the neighborhood I could suggest. It was Friday night and I really couldn't think of one. We had only lived in this neighborhood for about a year and I couldn't visualize any nice restaurants. I felt silly, but I really didn't know any.

"Well," Eli asked, "how far are you from Kennedy airport?" I didn't know the answer to that question either.

Eli thought there might be a nice place at the airport and then I remembered that I once had a drink in a pretty restaurant there.

"Yes!" I said, feeling a little more excited. "I do remember a place. . . ." My voice trailed off, but Eli was already getting up to leave.

We walked to where his car was parked and made the airport our destination. It probably took around a half hour to get there. On the way, I sat next to Eli in the front seat thinking how I wished that I was already on my way home. We made well-mannered conversation, parked in the airport lot and found the restaurant.

So there we were, seated across from each other, in a sophisticated atmosphere, at a spacious table with a clean white starched tablecloth. Behind Eli I could see a long view of part of the airport runway. When the waitress came to take our drink order, I ordered a glass of red wine, and Eli ordered a dry martini. As we sipped on our drinks, I began to relax just a little. The conversation was flowing. Eli was talkative and showed interest in me by asking a lot of questions, especially about all the different schools I had attended. Since I liked to talk, he made me feel more comfortable.

We had a full-course dinner and lingered over coffee and dessert. I thought that Eli was gracious and generous to offer dessert. I didn't have very many dates who took me out to such an elegant place. Also, it did feel so grown-up to be dining with a lawyer in a restaurant at the airport, a place where I had never eaten before. I loved experiencing new places.

We were seated across the table from each other, and we made a lot of eye contact. I could see, over Eli's shoulder, people passing the glass partition of the restaurant and my mind wandered. I thought that there must be many couples in love who were coming and going to far-off romantic places, like Rome or the Left Bank. Wouldn't that be wonderful? I drifted off a bit. When I came back to reality and to the face across the table from me, I was becoming less uncomfortable. I was easing up a little. It felt good to have a nice dinner with a new friend. It felt good to have someone to talk to.

How can I explain? Eli was not for me—but—he was filling some emptiness inside of me. I thought, hoped, that maybe he would fill a void in my life. I was essentially living alone, and I felt that emptiness every evening at dinner-time. By the time we were on our way back to my house, I had changed my mind from my first impression, when I had wondered how I would ever survive this evening. As I sank back into the softness of the front seat, satisfied and comfortable after dinner, it felt good to have shared a part of myself with this sophisticated fellow. I had changed my mind about Eli.

I felt very relieved that he didn't try to kiss me when we got home. I felt that he showed "respect," a quality my mother valued above all others in men, and that I believed I should value as well. Also, I was just more comfortable without any expectations from him. I was not intimidated. I knew that if he asked me out again I would accept.

When I went to bed that night, I lay on my back and looked up at the ceiling. In the darkness, I could see light from the streetlights in the back of the apartment building giving my bedroom a kind of glow I thought was hopeful. I knew that I had not fallen in love. I had not even fallen in like. But I had had a better evening than if I had stayed at home alone. I liked Eli's pleasant way of trying to be a good date. At least he tried. And although I was not attracted to him, perhaps he wasn't so bad after all.

As I lay in bed, I began to think about Alex. For two years we had been together, Alex and I, and it had been a time of great happiness and fun for me. Alex was my first boyfriend. And although I didn't know yet to say it, Alex had been my first love. I was too young to understand the complexities of love that could devastate you. But despite it all, I still wanted to be with him. I really wanted to be with Alex. Something inside my stomach twisted. His nickname was "Sonny." He always made me laugh. Where was he now? I missed him. I missed Alex.

These memories were so painful, and I knew there was no point to them. I forced my thoughts away from Alex and tried to think about Eli, who was the kind of man my mother would have approved of: Eli was from a wealthy family, from Brooklyn Heights. He went to Yale. He treated me like a lady, with the respect my mother so valued. Alex was only from a middle-class family from Ocean Avenue in Brooklyn. He didn't go to an Ivy League college. He wasn't as cultured as Eli. His father was a racetrack gambler. I thought Alex would turn out to be a gambler just like his father, since he always liked to take me to the racetrack, and he would often go there with his entire family on Sunday, their day out together.

I had decided that Alex was irresponsible. I knew that he wasn't very intelligent or even very interested in school. Trying to think like my mother, I concluded that Eli was better for me than Alex.

When I think back on it now, on that moment when I casually made a determination that would affect the rest of my life, picking a man as if I were shopping in a boutique at Bergdorf Goodman's, I can't even imagine who that girl was. They say hindsight is 20/20, but I just don't believe that. I have spent many hours thinking about her—that confused young woman who made such crucial choices so badly; I have invested so much time in trying to understand her and still she remains hazy in my memory. I know we are a product of the people we come from. If I tried to see through my mother's eyes, then clearly Eli Kramer was a "good match."

I lay in bed after my first date with Eli and thought about Alex, missed him, longed for him—his laugh, his kiss, his arms around me while we danced-—until I could bear it no longer. Because any thoughts of Alex inevitably led to the circumstances of our breakup, and I had made a career out of burying the memories of that last afternoon. So I forced myself away from thoughts of him, back to considering Eli. He seemed well mannered and mature. He seemed like the kind of man who would offer security, who would stay by me so I would never be alone again.

Eli said that he would call again. He didn't seem like the type to abandon himself or anyone else. He looked so centered and he talked like he knew things that I didn't. I got the feeling he knew a lot more about life than I did.

At least I have a new friend to look forward to seeing again, I thought.

～

A few days later, Eli called me for a second date, and asked me to the theatre. The Second City improvisation troupe was performing near his Greenwich Village apartment, and he had gotten us tickets for the upcoming Saturday evening. I accepted eagerly. I loved to go to the theatre.

When Saturday arrived, I got a last-minute telephone call, about an hour before Eli was supposed to pick me up.

"Myrna, it's Eli," he said when I answered the phone. "Listen, I have a problem. I can't start my car. Would you mind taking a taxi into the city to meet me?" Before I had a chance to respond, he added quickly "Of course I'll pay you back."

I felt just a tiny bit of impatience. For one thing, Queens was not Greenwich Village. I couldn't simply walk to the corner and hail a cab. I'd have to call a car service, reserve a car if one was available, and then wait downstairs for it to arrive. And it would cost about twenty-five dollars, which was exorbitant in 1962. But after checking to make sure Eli was aware of the cost, I agreed. Eli suggested we meet at his apartment and walk to the theatre from there. After taking down the address, I hung up.

But it didn't feel right, and it bothered me. I had been brought up by my mother to believe that men were supposed to come to the home of their date. I felt like Eli was asking me to compromise something I believed. It bothered me. I didn't believe Eli's car had broken down. I thought he was making that up because he didn't want to come out to Queens and get me. I felt that somehow, like with our first conversation about his height, Eli Kramer had played with the truth in order to get what he wanted. I thought about this in the car on the way to the city, but dismissed it. Here I was, wearing a pretty dress and heading toward a night at the theatre with a cultured older man, and these doubts about his character disturbed me. So I stuffed them down, hoping I was simply over reacting. I wanted Eli to like me. So I ignored the troubling evidence in favor of appearances. This was true to my training, and it was a pattern I would repeat again and again.

I wore a magenta raw silk dress with a plain rounded neckline, matching belt and a pleated skirt. An expensive-looking long string of pearls hung around my neck with pearl earrings to match. My medium height black patent leather heels with matching patent leather bag also went with the black shrug. It was 1962 and the era of the Jackie Kennedy look. I felt very much in style in this outfit. When we entered the theatre and people noticed us, I felt proud of myself and I walked tall. Eli looked like a lawyer in his dark suit and conservative tie.

We had a nice time at the theatre, and a second date led to a third. Soon, Eli Kramer and I were officially "dating."

Our dating relationship or so-called courtship took up a regular routine of once a week, usually Saturday night date. It was rare that we saw each other on a Friday or a Sunday or even in the afternoons. It was a rather formal courtship. In fact, when I wanted to have a casual date and wear jeans, Eli told me that he didn't even own a pair.

I got to know more about Eli and his profession as a lawyer. Eli was in partnership with a law school classmate and it seemed as if Eli's success was assured. Eli's group of friends from Yale Law School, and the Yale Club where he was a member also impressed me a great deal.

Dating Eli exposed me to a world of wealth, privilege and glamour which attracted me. I liked the things we did— the elegant French restaurants, the theatre, the glittering cocktail parties with his friends. Eli's credentials—his Ivy League education, family money, professional status and sophisticated interests, and the equally polished friends who shared them—brought with them a certain status which I felt spilled over onto me when I was with him. I liked the way I felt being with him more than I ever liked Eli, but at the time I didn't recognize the distinction.

Respect, my mother had drilled into both my sister and me, was something a man showed for a woman by protecting her chastity, and so I believed that the notable lack of touching between Eli and me was his way of respecting me. My feelings about this ranged from gratitude to confusion; from acceptance to, sometimes, frustration. After five months of dating, with one exception our physical relationship hadn't advanced past a single, dry goodnight kiss.

I lived for romance that never came, and ignored the fact that when Eli kissed me, it just wasn't the right chemistry. Something was entirely different from when I kissed my first boyfriend, Alex. I was aware of Eli's crooked teeth and there wasn't any passion between us. I tried to respond in a romantic way. I told myself that I should enjoy this and I acted as if I did. I was trying to do the right thing but I knew deep inside that something was wrong.

Then came the ultimatum. Eli and I had been dating less than six months, consistently spending most Saturday nights together. So I was completely surprised when,

while out for a late night supper at an Italian restaurant on
Queens Boulevard, Eli told me he thought he was falling
in love with me. I sat all the way back in my seat with my
spine erect, and almost fell over.

"And I don't want you to go out with anyone else," Eli
continued. I felt at a loss for words. I didn't want to hurt
his feelings, but I knew I didn't share them.

"Look Eli," I finally said, trying to be very clear. "I don't
go steady. I was never pinned in college and I don't want to
be pinned down to one person." His face was blank and I
hurried on." It's not that I don't like you. I do like you. But
I can't make that kind of a commitment."

"Why not?" he asked.

"I don't want to get married until I'm at least thirty," I
answered. "I don't believe that people get to know who they
really are until at least thirty." I was barely twenty-three at
the time, and I knew this was true. I knew I didn't have
a clue yet who I was. I felt like a receptacle for the values
and beliefs of everyone who had surrounded me all my life:
family, teachers, friends, my mother, my father, my best
friend Marianne, Alex.

"Well, I want to date you exclusively," Eli continued as if
I hadn't spoken. "It doesn't mean that we're engaged. But I
don't want you to go out with anyone else."

"I can't do that," I told him. And he broke up with me.

"Any time you change your mind," he said, "call me and
I'll be happy to hear from you."

Several weeks passed and my father came home after a
weekend at The Concord Hotel at Kiamesha Lake, in the
Catskill Mountains of upstate New York. He told me that
Eli was there on a "singles" weekend and was very friendly.
All of a sudden I felt a little twinge of jealousy. So, I decided
to call Eli. After the usual hellos, I told him I missed him
and wanted to try dating him exclusively.

"But it doesn't mean that we're engaged," I made sure to remind him.

An agreement was made, and we started dating again. Only this time, there was a commitment, and I felt it. I was getting used to having Eli in my life. It wasn't a big surprise when one night he proposed to me and I accepted.

CHAPTER SIX

On one typical Saturday night, when Eli arrived to pick me up, he came into the apartment, put his hand into his pocket and took out a crumpled tissue. He opened it and held it in front of my face.

"Here's the diamond," he said, excited.

"What?" I said as I stepped closer. I didn't know what he meant. Eli had opened the tissue and I looked inside the crumpled wad. And there was a stone that looked like a diamond. And it sparkled.

"My father got a great buy on this," Eli continued, his face lit up with a huge smile. "It's a little under four carats and it's almost perfect. It's worth one and a half times what he paid for it."

I was totally taken aback. We had just gotten engaged last week and we hadn't discussed anything at all about rings. I knew nothing about this shopping spree. I felt very uncomfortable and angry. This was not the way I imagined it would be. I took a deep breath and tried to control my irritation.

"I wanted to go to the store with you," I said. "I wanted us to pick it out together." I pushed away his outstretched hand, the large diamond still lying there incongruously in the white tissue. "I don't care what a great buy this is. I don't want it." Eli stood there, listening, looking disappointed and slightly impatient. "I don't even like the pear shape," I continued. "It's *my* ring, and what I'd really like is a marquis shape."

Something was happening here, and I knew it was important; I knew it was important to make Eli think of *me*, his future wife, whom he claimed to love; not of bargains, nor of his father, nor of convenience or payback favors, nor of whatever it was that made him bring me this diamond in a tissue, but of me, and us.

I looked into his eyes and continued. "Eli, whatever the ring turns out to be, I want us to pick it out together, like an engaged couple should. Don't you think so?"

He agreed and I felt relieved. "I'll bring the stone back to my father and see if he can return it," Eli said.

About a week later, Eli said his father had returned the first diamond and we could go shopping for a ring. He wanted to start at a jewelry store his father had recommended on Forty-second Street. I didn't care where we started. I was so happy we were doing this together, as a couple.

I grew up on notions of romance. I was not alone in this. So many young girls, then and now, aspire to a romantic ideal of love and search for the relationship that seems to meet it. We want what we see—on television, in movies and theater, and even, if we are lucky, romance modeled in our own families. I devoured romantic poetry—Elizabeth Barrett Browning, Shakespeare's sonnets, Keats—and was as drawn to the lives of the poets, their tenderness and deep love, as I was to the verse itself. I listened to the sentimental love songs of the time about princes arriving to sweep me off my feet and took them deeply to heart.

I never let go of those dreams. And even though I knew Eli was not the prince who populated them; even though there was nothing between us *fashioned of starlight*, I kept hoping romance would bloom between us, despite its glaring absence in all of our interactions. Even Eli's "proposal" was a mere formality. By the time he asked me to marry him, he had already been telling his friends and family we were engaged, and he took my acceptance for granted. I couldn't shake the sense that Eli saw me as the most qualified applicant for an unfilled position in his life, that of wife. He was thirty-two years old, and his younger brother was already married and had a child. His friends were all married or engaged. His father expected him to marry and produce grandsons. Eli's life had always been mapped out for him: the right school, the right career, the right wife wearing the right diamond on her finger, the right apartment in the right neighborhood. For the most part he had stayed the course as he was meant to, but he was a little behind in finding a wife.

But I wanted to be married. I wanted to be a wife, it was what I had been raised to do and be. My education had always been presented to me as a safety net, something to fall back on if, and only if, I needed it, and I accepted that. So I prepared myself to become Eli's wife, ignoring my misgivings, hoping it would be fine. I felt old at twenty-three, and afraid that if I didn't seize this chance, I would never have another. In my deepest heart, I knew Eli wouldn't ever satisfy my need for passion. But I ignored the truth and lived on hope.

The day we went shopping for my engagement ring, Eli and I got to the store and the man behind the counter was expecting us. He took out a tray with exactly three diamond engagement rings rolling around on dark velvet.

"You can pick out one of these," he told me. "They're all good buys, but," he pointed to one "this one is the best buy."

They were all pear-shaped. The so-called best buy was put into my hand to examine. I was confused and disappointed.

"Are there any marquis-shaped rings I could see?" I asked politely, only to be informed by both the salesman and Eli that I could choose only one of the three diamonds before me on the velvet covered tray. My feelings or preferences did not mean anything at all. This was not the romantic sharing experience I had thought it would be. This was commerce, business, bargain-hunting. This was just the same as presenting me with a diamond in a tissue. An engagement ring is important. It is the ring I would wear for the rest of my life as a symbol of our love, but Eli seemed more concerned with getting his father's approval. I would have rather had a small diamond we picked out together. I stared down at these three glittering jewels before me, defeated, and, even though both Eli and the salesman didn't approve of my choice, I picked the biggest one.

As soon as we were formally engaged, plans were made. Eli's roommate, also a graduate of Yale, planned an informal engagement party in their apartment on Bleecker Street. It was a two-bedroom, one bath apartment with a large living room and foyer. More than forty people showed up with lots of bottles of wine and a few presents. There were several kinds of dips. Grape leaves were new to me and they soon disappeared. There was a lot of noise and as Eli introduced me to some of the other people, I felt more like a trophy than anything else. I didn't know most of these people but I did my best to be as sociable as possible. It was my first "official" appearance as Eli's fiancée and I wanted to do the right thing.

After a few hours of socializing, Eli came to me where I was chatting with a group of his friends. He grabbed my hand, whispered, "It's time to go into the bedroom" and led me into his housemate's bedroom. I didn't know what "It's time to go into the bedroom" meant. Eli had said it as if we had an appointment. But I followed him quietly.

We went over to the bed. Perhaps we got undressed but I really don't remember taking off any clothes. I do vaguely remember that Eli got on top of me. I don't think he entered me. He moved around a little and made some noises. I don't really know what happened sexually. It was over before I had even understood what Eli was doing. Aside from some dry kissing and the one time Eli had touched my breast, this was the most physical he had ever been with me, and I had no idea what had just happened. I lay on the bed as Eli rolled off me, and I could see him hunched over and cleaning himself with his ever-present handkerchief. I didn't know what he had just done or why, but I knew I was supposed to feel as if something monumental had just happened, as if I had just been "taken" or marked somehow. But I had felt nothing. I was still fully dressed, still lying on the bed when Eli finally turned to me.

"Have you ever been to bed with anyone else?" he asked me. "Have you ever had sex before?" I was so confused I didn't know what to say. Did these questions mean that Eli thought what we had just done was "going to bed?" Did he think the two-minute dry hump he had just performed on top of me was sex? I knew it wasn't. I thought about his questions for a long while.

"Yes," I finally answered with no elaboration. Although, at the same moment, that rape, that day on Alex's parents' bed flashed across the inside of my head. Instant headache.

"Who?" Eli asked as he tucked in his rumpled shirt. He wasn't looking at me as I told him.

"Don't you ever tell anyone else," he hissed. "Promise me!" He was vehement. "Promise me that you won't ever tell anyone."

I agreed. There didn't seem to be anything else to do. Eli opened the bedroom door and we went back to the party and the noise.

That night I just couldn't make sense out of what happened in the bedroom. I don't think anything really happened. At least not for me. And I wondered what really had happened for Eli. It would have been completely out of character, for either one of us, to talk about what this retarded sexual experience meant. But what I suspected— that Eli had dry humped me at our engagement party because he felt obligated to have some sort of sexual experience with me before we married, and that it was this sense of obligation, not to me but to his self-image as a man, that motivated him—was too upsetting for me to examine on my own, and I had no one to confide in, especially the man I was about to marry.

Neither one of us ever mentioned this experience again.

I was in denial over my situation. I didn't want to admit the truth, but knew: *This match is a big mistake. It is not the right one.* I wished that I had a mother who was there to talk to. I was too embarrassed to talk to my father or even a girlfriend. So I said and I did nothing.

I had been trained to believe that the physical demands made by men were a chore of marriage, and by this logic, Eli's disinterest in me sexually could be interpreted as a good thing. Clinging to this warped logic was like clutching a life preserver. It was all I had to go on.

Eli Kramer was a "good catch," and for girls of my class and station, more than education or career or life experience, a good catch was what we aspired to. I was meant to be married. We all were. Marrying well meant being successful at our assigned task: being a wife.

I set my sights on my wedding day as the magic borderline. Once it was crossed, Eli and I would be free to be passionate. Such was the transforming power I was raised to believe marriage had. We set the date: August 25, 1963.

⁓

It was mostly circumstantial that I chose August 25 as my wedding date, but I was pleased with it. It was the same date as the wedding date of my best friend Marianne one year earlier. Marianne and I had met our freshman year at Bennington, when we pledged the same sorority, and we had developed a strong bond. Our friendship grew over two years at Bennington, and for junior year, we went together to study in Spain. We were roommates in Spain and classmates again, senior year, at NYU. After graduation, Marianne met and married a lawyer, and I was a bridesmaid. The day Marianne got married felt like the day I lost my best friend. That was my understanding of marriage, a statement of allegiance. While I knew Marianne and I could still be friends, I also knew that her husband would become her first priority. I felt that the only way to regain the closeness and stability that our relationship had provided would be to do what Marianne did and find a husband. So I did, and began the process of planning a wedding by picking a date—the same date Marianne had picked.

My father announced that he would give me a wedding gift of $5,000. He told me that I could use it for anything I wanted: a wedding, a honeymoon, furniture for our new home or "if you just want to open the window and throw it out, it's yours to do with as you wish."

Eli and I began looking at spaces to hold our wedding. We priced my favorite hotel, the Park Lane on Park Avenue, and also the Waldorf Astoria on the next block, and soon realized that with the number of people we would need to invite, the $5,000 wedding gift would be spent in one night. And I realized I didn't care that much about a big wedding. I wanted to be able to buy furniture for our new home. Eli agreed with me.

However, when Eli's father heard that there wasn't going to be a big wedding for his eldest son, he offered to make the wedding himself and pay for everything at his synagogue in Brooklyn. When Eli told me this, my initial reaction was to refuse the offer. It felt disrespectful to my father, who had given me both money and choice. And it made the occasion seem not about us, but about Fred and his need to impress people with his wealth and status.

When I told my decision to my father and my sister, they thought I was making a big mistake. Why not let him make the wedding, they said; think of all the expensive wedding gifts you'll get. So what if *you* don't want to get married at his temple. Don't be a jerk!

Well, I certainly didn't want to be a jerk. So, I changed my mind, thanked Fred for his generous offer, and proceeded, as much as I could, to plan my wedding.

So many choices now had to be made: the list of people to invite, the kosher caterer, florist and of course, the engraved wedding invitations:

Mrs. Lillian Jacobs Kaye
and
Mr. Irving Kaye
request the honor of your presence
at the marriage of their daughter
Myrna

to
Mr. Elias F. Kramer
Saturday, the twenty-fifth of August
at half after six o'clock. . . .

At the same time that all of these arrangements were being made, there was the big news that my wedding plans irritated my sister Sandra. At the time, we were all living together in Queens. Sandra had returned from Oberlin College, and my father was traveling much less. Our apartment was a small, two-bedroom/one bath. Sandra and I shared a bedroom, and she didn't want me there when she returned home. She felt it would be "too much disturbance" and would interfere with her life, and my father agreed.

"The house is not big enough for the two of you," he said when he told me I'd have to leave. "Sandra needs quiet and peace. I'm sorry. I hope you understand." I didn't, actually. I was still in school, and busy with wedding plans. I didn't know what this "disturbance" was that so concerned Sandra. I wasn't home that much.

My father offered to pay for a "reasonably priced sublet" where I could stay until I got married, so, with no other choice, I moved out of the apartment in Queens, and would never return.

It was three months until my wedding, and I spent it like a vagabond. I found a sublet in the West Village, but had to leave when the tenant came back early. From there I went to a nearby residential hotel. It was creepy and roach infested, and one night I called my father and begged him to let me come home.

"Please, please," I said to him on the telephone. "I want to sleep in my own bed. I can't stand it here." I was near tears, but he was firm in his belief that my presence would negatively affect Sandra's health.

At the beginning of August, I moved to the Prince George Hotel in downtown Brooklyn. It was very close to the synagogue, where wedding preparations were being finalized. My mother, who had moved to Los Angeles after she left my father, arrived in town to help me get ready for my wedding, and wound up staying with me at the hotel. The Prince George was much nicer than the place I had been staying, and much more expensive. By this time, the cost of the hotel and meals were both coming out of my $5,000 wedding present.

Since my mother was working at Saks Fifth Avenue in Los Angeles, she was able to get a discount at the New York store, which I had already taken advantage of. I ordered my gown, headpiece and shoes at Saks. I also bought my so-called trousseau for my honeymoon: shoes and a bag and a few dresses. I still saw Eli for our regular Saturday night date. I socialized with his friends and talked about the wedding plans. Sometimes I would look at Eli and think he was more like a co-worker than a lover. Although I tried to ignore it, my uneasiness increased as our wedding date approached.

August 25 arrived. My mother and I got ourselves to the Jewish Center on time. We had to be there at least an hour earlier to dress with the rest of the wedding party. Lillian wore a very simple sky blue sleeveless sheath with my long cultured pearls, and she was a nervous wreck. Her histrionics made me so very impatient. It really was me who should have been nervous. But that was my mother. Every occasion was about her. Even her daughter's wedding.

My two bridesmaids were Marianne and Irene, another friend I had made during our junior year in Barcelona. They wore matching gowns and they had sprayed green flowers to go with their outfits. My two sisters-in-law were there with their husbands. All the ushers and Eli's brother, the best man, were formally dressed in tuxedos and the women were in gowns. My soon-to-be father-in-law, Fred, who was all of five feet tall, was swaggering about in a black tux, puffed up and bossy. I can still picture him vividly. "I look like a penguin in this suit," he complained. And the truth is that he really did.

I was standing with Sandra when we were given a fifteen-minute warning signal. I felt a little nervous. Sandra was my maid of honor, although things had been rather strained between us. I was still hurt and confused by the fact that she had banished me from our home, but she was my sister, and I was glad she was with me. As we waited for the procession to begin, she fussed with my gown and then, to my surprise, she said "Myrna, it's not too late to change your mind."

In that instant, I visualized myself tearing off that gorgeous long veil and headpiece and running out of the synagogue, down the steps, as fast as I could. My heart started to race. Sandra was watching me intently.

"I can't," I said wearily to my sister.

"Why not?" she asked. But I was already denying my heart, forcing it back into the dark cupboard where I had trained myself to keep it. Already I was thinking of practicalities and appearances: Fred would be furious about all the money he'd spent; my mother would have a nervous breakdown; I'd be embarrassed in front of all these guests: Fred's wealthy colleagues and temple members; Eli's Yale friends. I'd have to return all those expensive wedding gifts, with some sort of explanation, and I didn't want to do that. I shivered even though it was a warm evening, and the image of escape flashed once more before my eyes. I could see my hand reaching up to tear off the veil. And then the image screeched to a halt, frozen by reality. I knew that I wouldn't be able to remove that headpiece, which was embedded with hairpins into my bird's nest hairstyle. That was a popular style in 1963. And thinking of my hair brought me back to reality. I couldn't get out of this marriage. I couldn't even get out of this costume.

"I have to do this," I finally said to Sandra, and that was what I believed. I had no home, no place to go even if I did run from that temple. And no one to go to. I had found the vagabond existence I endured in the months before my wedding to be frightening and uncomfortable. If I didn't marry Eli, I thought, that would be my life forever. My father was no longer going to be there as my protector.

The processional music began. .

The wedding party was led to the door at the entrance to the large auditorium.

And then it was my turn.

The room was filled with lots of people and lots of flowers. I was on. I walked down the aisle. I don't remember the rest until it was my turn to answer.

"I do."

∽

It was a soup-to-nuts elegant Saturday night formal affair in a reception room with immense crystal chandeliers. In full regalia, the women danced to the live music in long gowns with their diamonds and jewels led by their tuxedoed partners. There were about 200 people and everything went smoothly except for the end of the evening. My father drank too much, and he wasn't in any condition to drive himself home. Eli and I drove him home and then we went straight to the motel airport, as we had a very early flight the next morning to Acapulco. When we got to our room, I remember that Eli gleefully emptied checks and cash all over the bed from his pants pockets, his inside vest pocket as well as the regular outside pockets. I stood there feeling irrelevant as my new husband ignored me and began sorting and counting the crumpled bills and checks which drifted across the bedspread.

I remember Eli counted it all up and seemed to be a little disappointed. I was disappointed too, but for a completely different reason. I said nothing, but moved to the mirror and considered my complicated hairdo. I wasn't sure I even knew how to dismantle it. I was gazing at myself but thinking about Acapulco and how I hoped it would be beautiful and romantic. I was thinking about the pretty new clothes I'd bought, including new lingerie. And then I heard Eli behind me.

"We have to do it," Eli said. "Let's get undressed."

It took a beat before I understood that "it" meant sex, and I was so flustered and embarrassed I didn't know what to do. This wasn't the way I had imagined it and I hurried towards my suitcase. Eli was taking off his clothes as I unzipped the bag.

"I have to put on my new peignoir set," I told him, searching through my neatly packed clothes. I was trying so hard to preserve some semblance of romance. I didn't know how to abandon the scenario I had imagined: we would kiss and snuggle on the bed, giggling and talking about the wedding. Then I would rise and go into the bathroom. When I came out, looking sweet and sexy in my new lingerie, my husband would be waiting eagerly for me in bed. He would tell me how beautiful I looked and then we would make love.

I dashed into the bathroom and put on the nightgown and matching robe, and then hurried back to join him on the bed. He was naked and covered by the sheet.

Eli just wanted to get on top of me so all I had to do was to lift up the bottom of the nightgown above my waist. I couldn't see his body and he couldn't see mine, and when he entered me, I couldn't feel anything except for the hairpins sticking into my scalp as he moved forward and backward, each time knocking my head against the headboard. It took so many hairpins to hold my hairdo in place that each time Eli moved forward and back, the hairpins moved along with him. It hurt a lot, but when I tried to tell him, he didn't seem to hear me.

It was a nightmare instead of a wedding night.

We were both tired and fell quickly asleep without any other talking, touching, or sharing. The sound of the telephone woke us up. Eli flew out of bed and answered the wake-up call.

"Get up. Get up!" he ordered. "We don't want to miss the flight."

I must have been exhausted. I can remember my eyelids felt as if they were pasted to the bottom lids. I had to literally force my eyes to open. We got dressed quickly and made our plane to the famous honeymoon hotel, in Acapulco, Mexico.

It was a beautiful place, and we stayed in a detached villa with a small private swimming pool, which thrilled me. I love the water and I loved to swim. However, Eli didn't want to put on a bathing suit and he wouldn't join me in the pool. After a couple of days, I can remember begging him, calling up at him as he stood above me at the edge of the pool.

"Eli," I called to him, trying to be sweet and appealing, "please come in and be with me." But he just said no. He wouldn't come in, and I thought he probably was embarrassed about his pudgy body. But I didn't know what to do to make him feel better. The truth was he didn't have a very good build, but we were on our honeymoon and I wanted so badly to feel close to my husband. I didn't care about his body. I wished he could relax and try to share something with me.

So I stayed in the pool alone. I tried to enjoy it but I felt gypped. I wanted to have fun, and this was not any fun.

We went out for dinner every night, many times at the fancy dining room with open walls to the outside.. I really enjoyed getting dressed in different new pretty dresses for dinner. My skin bronzed in the sun. It would have been a perfect honeymoon except that my husband never touched me.

My scalp was still sensitive from our wedding night consummation, and there had been nothing since. No kissing or cuddling. No sex. I didn't know what to think, and I was completely ill equipped to deal with this problem. Eli and I had virtually no physical relationship before we married, but I had thought the reason for this was *because* we weren't married. I thought once we wed, we would do what married couples were allowed to do: make love, explore each other's bodies, satisfy each other. I knew so little about sex and men, and what I did know was confused. But I had these feelings. I had desires. I was married now and I wanted a satisfying physical relationship with my husband. We were in this idyllic setting; romance was everywhere. We had a private villa and a king-sized bed. But every night we politely said goodnight and went to sleep on our own side. There was an ocean between us.

One morning as we both lay awake with our eyes closed in the king-sized bed, I thought about how lucky we were to be in this luxurious place, I knew that there was a thermos of freshly made coffee and seasonal fresh fruit right outside our front door, as there was every morning. We had a refrigerator stocked with drinks and juices, and a sparkling private swimming pool. Every day there was a spectacular sunrise and equally gorgeous sunset. It was paradise. But I felt upset. I had been waiting for days for Eli to make some kind of a physical advance. I rolled over and looked at my husband with sleepy eyes.

"Good morning," I whispered in what I hoped was a sexy voice. His eyes were closed but I knew he was awake. Without looking at me, he returned my greeting.

But not another word. I was dumbfounded. I lay there with my eyes closed not knowing what to do.

I thought about my father, about how he had always been my source of advice and comfort. Whenever I was confronting a thorny problem, I could go to him and explain the dilemma, certain that he would listen carefully and share the benefit of his wisdom. I decided to think about what my father might suggest in this situation. I closed my eyes and thought, *Daddy, what should I do? Eli hasn't made any overture toward me. This is our honeymoon.* And as I thought about my father, I got my answer.

You be the big one. You make the first move.

All right. I gathered up all of my nerve and rolled over, crossing that sea of bed between us. My body brushed lightly against Eli, and I reached over and tentatively caressed his shoulder.

There was not even the tiniest response. After a couple of seconds, he rolled over and away from me. It felt as if my heart went into the ground. I didn't know what to do.

I lay still and silent for a few minutes, trying to control my emotions. Finally I spoke.

"Why did you roll away from me?" I asked Eli.

Silence. Complete and heavy silence for a couple of minutes. My heart was breaking. I didn't know what to do. I noticed a small salamander on the wall close to the side where Eli was.

"Eli!" I said, my voice rising. "Look, there's a salamander near you—on the wall." I seized on the presence of this little lizard as an opportunity to distract myself from what had just happened. I overreacted to it because I couldn't bear to keep thinking of the way in which I had just been rejected.

"Eli!" I said again, poking him. "Do something. Get it away." My voice had an unpleasant whine to it. I knew this had nothing to do with the salamander. Eli did not move. Like the salamander, he was just frozen.

I was so hurt and angry and I didn't know what to do. The seconds ticked by. Nothing. Stillness. So, in order to break this heavy *doom*, I searched for a way to hurt Eli back.

"I don't like that salamander" I finally said. "It's ugly. Like you." Silence from the other side of the king-sized bed. "I'm going to call you salamander from now on," I continued, my voice low and mean. "Salamander. That's your nickname."

All I could think of at that moment was how I could hurt Eli the way he'd just hurt me.

"Salamander," I hissed again.

And that's how the rest of our honeymoon went. Nothing at all between us. No touching. But I still hoped that when we got to Acapulco, things would be different.

Eli liked margaritas, and took advantage of cheap, good tequila which was available everywhere. Sometimes I had a few drinks with him, but tequila didn't really agree with me. One evening when we returned to our room in Acapulco, after spending some time in the hotel bar, I had to sit up in my twin bed.

"Eli," I called to him, "I'm dizzy. I can't close my eyes." I had the spins.

But Eli didn't hear me. He was already asleep, snoring loudly. I put one foot on the floor to try and steady the whirling room, and choked back tears. It felt like some sort of sick, ironic joke. I got married because I didn't want to be lonely. I lay there fighting off nausea and listening to Eli snore from the other twin bed. How could I be on my honeymoon with a husband who doesn't lay a hand on me, who doesn't even want to talk to me?

After three weeks, we caught our flight back to New York City. As the plane was landing at the airport, I knew that I really did not have a good marriage. I also knew that we had a rental lease on a two-bedroom, two-bath apartment where my mother had been staying while we were gone. I also knew that I felt as if I didn't have any other place to go. No home. Nobody, except for my absentee father.

What should I do? I reminded myself that I had taken a vow and I had really meant it—till death do us part, for richer or for poorer. I believed in that vow. I believed in marriage. As our plane touched down on the New York runway, I turned to my husband.

"We're here," I said sweetly to Eli. "We made it."

Eli worked six days and six nights per week, and I spent more time than I wanted alone in our large, silent apartment. Many weekday evenings, I would make a wonderful dinner and at the last minute, Eli would call and tell me he had to work that night. So, I would invite my old roommate Ann, who was now living around the corner, to come for dinner. I can remember spending hours with Ann on the telephone. It was always a warm, happy conversation with lots of laughs, but I silently wished that it was Eli I could talk with this way. I spent days alone and nights miserable, lying untouched next to my sleeping husband, my frustration and despair keeping me awake. In desperation, I called my father and sister and asked if we could get together and have "a walk and a talk."

We met one early spring afternoon and walked along the East River promenade. I told them about how Eli and

I had no sex life. I described our dry, distant relationship and tried to express how confused and unhappy I was.

"Myrna," my father said. "People don't change. Either it's there or it's not. It isn't something you can *put* there." I listened to my father with rising dismay. He was telling me it was hopeless.

"Daddy," Sandra snapped. "Let Myrna decide for herself. It's her life, her marriage." The stigma of the divorcee, in 1963, was far more powerful than it is today. To be divorced at twenty-three, to have failed at marriage, the thing I was bred for, was more than I could bear. No, I was not ready to take my father's advice. I'm going to make this marriage work, I thought, *if it kills me.*

Each night, as Eli lay snoring in a separate bed on the same headboard, overdosed on coffee and cake and the eleven o'clock news, I watched television, restless and tense. Often my thoughts would turn, seemingly of their own volition, to sex, and I would fantasize that there were two sexy men in my bed with me. There was one making love to me above the waist and another making love to me below the waist. Sometimes I would masturbate as secretly and quietly as I could while thinking of these two men. I imagined hungry moans and sweat drenched embraces, tangled bodies and probing tongues. I imagined losing control, giving myself over entirely to desire. I wished I didn't have to rely on these two imaginary lovers to satisfy me. I never shared this fantasy with anyone else.

Unfortunately, I never did act it out either.

Finally the day arrived when Eli came home and told me that it was now time, since two years had passed and our marriage was good, to have a baby. I knew he was wrong about the state of our marriage, but I didn't care. I definitely wanted to have children and I felt that everything in our relationship would be much better if we had a baby.

Some people just aren't developed inside. Eli was, and is, I assume, as underdeveloped emotionally, socially, and spiritually as he was physically. He distanced himself from me in mind, body and heart, and I was withering away from inattention. It's no wonder I wanted a baby so badly.

That night, we made a concerted effort to conceive. In bed, I concentrated on the baby we were making as I crawled on top of my husband. My curly hair cascaded down over my shoulders as I guided one of his hands to my breast.

"I want to make a baby," I whispered.

"So do I," he responded, and reached for me.

It lasted only a few minutes, and when it was over I lay with my eyes closed, focusing entirely on the bud of a child I felt sure was growing in my womb. "I can just feel it," I told Eli. I don't think he believed me. Five weeks later, as soon as I could, I had a pregnancy test. The day I got the results, I waited impatiently for Eli to come home.

"I'm pregnant!" I joyfully sang as soon as he walked through the door.

CHAPTER SEVEN

My pregnancy was confirmed in the fall of 1965, and I was ecstatic. I had such hopes for this baby, for the change in my life it would bring: a sense of purpose, closeness between me and my husband, someone to love, who would love me unconditionally. I was twenty-five years old, and I couldn't wait to be a mother.

I'm sure I'm not the only woman who, when contemplating first time motherhood, believes naively that mothering will "come naturally." Without a doubt there is an immediate bond, a kind of internal knowing, between mother and child. I felt it with all three of my sons. And without a doubt, there is a deep desire to protect and nurture your baby. But how to do that—the specifics of how to be a mother, how to know what your child needs, how to cope with the long periods of uncertainty, or boredom, or frustration; how to efficiently change a diaper, all of that, I believe, has to be taught somehow, or modeled. I never had a model of nurturing. I prepared for my baby's arrival as best I knew how. I shopped and made lists and saw my doctor regularly. But I had no idea how to prepare emotionally for the

complete renovation of my life as I knew it which motherhood, by its very nature, requires. Absent mothers raise
unprepared daughters.

Since the removal of an ovary along with an ovarian
cyst and my appendix at the age of 20, I always thought I'd
have trouble conceiving and having more than one child.
But still, I always wanted and expected to have at least two
children. I thought about how I wouldn't be like my "bad"
mother. I would never send my children away to boarding
schools like the ones I went to. In fleeting moments, I think
I envisioned a little girl who looked like me when I was little,
to whom I would give the love that I had always yearned
for, but never received.

I thought it was easy to be a good mother. I was wrong.

I luckily went through my pregnancy in denial of this
history lurking in the back of my mind and was actually
feeling very well and very happy. I was addicted to cigarettes and smoking more than a pack a day. Smoking cigarettes in 1966 was a more or less acceptable vice, although
admittedly it wasn't healthy and I knew deep down that
they couldn't possibly be good for the baby or for me. But,
I was very addicted to the nicotine. The only good thing
about smoking cigarettes was that it prevented me from
gaining a lot of extra weight. I was small and carried to the
front, which I believed (correctly, it turned out) meant that
I was carrying a boy. I was so happy to know I was going
to have a son. I thought that the picture of a perfect family
was first a son and then a daughter. The girl would always
have an older brother, someone she could ask questions of
and who would always be her protector.

The months passed peacefully. I anticipated that having
a son and a family would change the tone of my life. As it
got closer to my expected delivery date, it was time to order
a layette. To Bloomingdale's, to the baby department I went.

I wore a comfortable pretty white sleeveless dress with pink and red poppies, which showed off my suntan. I had long, naturally curly hair and I knew I looked pretty, I felt proud of my good health and proud of my bulging beach-ball stomach. I had always heard that pregnant women "glowed," but most of the ones I'd seen looked uncomfortable and out of proportion. But I really felt like I was glowing with health, happiness and anticipation.

My list of baby clothes and miscellaneous items to purchase and gifts to register for was compiled by asking other mothers and reading. I went armed with my written list. It was such a feeling of accomplishment for me to leave Bloomingdale's having completed this project the best way I knew how, on my own.

I took the Lamaze course in natural childbirth. I read whatever books were available. I even requested a private tour of the hospital room so I could see the delivery table and most importantly, the "stirrups" where I would have to put my feet. I knew that this was going further than most other expectant mothers, but my mother had scared the shit out of me. *I bore you,* she used to snap at me when she was annoyed. *I gave birth to you and this is the thanks I get?* For most of my childhood, I believed that I had done something wrong simply by being born; as if something I did caused childbirth to hurt my mother so much. She would describe the process of childbirth like it was the worst and most painful experience one could ever have.

I tried to educate myself and to find out the truth by talking with other mothers and my doctor, and reading books. I decided to learn how to breathe naturally and give birth without being put out and to see the baby being born. I registered for a couple's natural birth course at a local hospital, but when Eli came to take the course with me, he made me feel awkward and uncomfortable. I didn't feel that I would really be able to depend on him for his love and support in unexpected moments of need and duress. Although I finished the course, I didn't expect to seriously follow through with this method.

My bag was packed. My due date loomed. False trips to the hospital were made by expectant mothers whose contractions weren't timed at regular intervals. The one thing I knew I didn't want to do was to make a false trip to the hospital. I told myself that I was not going to do that. I had already experienced some irregular contractions, but I knew what they were. I felt calm, prepared and in control. I felt so proud of myself. I felt the little girl in me sticking her tongue out at my mother: *See? I can do this. I can do what you couldn't.*

Mitchell was born on a Sunday in June. I was having contractions, but they were spaced at regular intervals. I felt so mature and experienced.

"I think I'm getting regular contractions," I told Eli. "I'm going upstairs to the sunroof to time them and read a book."

I relaxed on my chaise, timing my contractions and trying to read my book. I was so proud of myself. I did that for a few hours and wrote down the intervals between the beginning of one contraction and the start of the next. Although it was a few days before my due date, the pains were coming regularly.

When I came downstairs from the roof, I put the two steaks I had bought for dinner in the wall oven, told Eli about the contractions and called my gynecologist. He wasn't there. I left a message with his answering service. My contractions were five minutes apart.

Eli and I sat down to eat. Just as I had taken a couple of bites, the doctor called back. When I told him the timing of the contractions, he told me to stop eating and go directly to the emergency room of the hospital.

I hung up the phone and returned to the dinner table. "What did he say?" Eli asked. I took a bite of my steak.

"He said to stop eating," I said. "He said don't eat any more and go directly to the hospital." I was calmly cutting my steak and chewing it as I repeated the doctor's words. Eli was looking at me as if I were crazy. "But," I continued, "if you think I'm going to waste a good steak like this, you're wrong."

Eli looked a little panicky. "Stop!" he nearly shouted. "Don't eat anything else."

I did not listen to either one of them. I cannot remember why, except that I suddenly felt anxious and when I get anxious, I feel hungry. I was also looking forward to eating the steak I had purchased, and I didn't want to waste it. So I finished eating the rest of that big steak. Then I went into my room to get dressed to go to the hospital.

My bag had been packed and ready for a couple of days, and Eli carried it as we took the elevator down to the lobby. We took a taxi and I can remember having a very strong and sharp contraction as we went over a pothole right on Fifty-seventh Street. There were a couple of other very strong ones before we finally arrived at the emergency entrance. After I was admitted and rushed to a private room, the resident came in.

"Your doctor is on his way to the hospital," the young man told me as he prepared to do a pelvic exam. A quick exploration and he informed me that my cervix was almost fully dilated and I was about to go into the last part of my labor. My first feeling was relief and pride. This hadn't been a false trip. I had done well. But these satisfied feelings were quickly replaced by terror. Something was happening I didn't understand.

"Oh no!" I moaned. "What is that?" I struggled to sit up and see the resident. "Please, I'm scared. I'm scared stiff."

"Your water just broke," he said, smiling. "That's good because it happened naturally. It'll be soon." I remember that he seemed so calm and matter of fact as he moved around my hospital bed, but I was getting more and more frightened as my contractions got stronger and the pain washed over me. Everything I had learned in my childbirth classes became irrelevant in light of this sharp, consuming pain. First time childbirth is an experience you really can't prepare for.

"Please put me out," I begged the resident frantically. "I don't want natural childbirth. I changed my mind. I don't want any pain. I don't want to feel anything." He looked at me kindly, still perfectly calm and collected, despite my rising panic. He nodded and reached for an anesthetic, which had apparently been prepared just in case.

"Sing a song," he said as he swabbed me.

"What?"

"Choose any song you like and sing it."

I didn't have a clue why he wanted me to sing, but if that was what one needed to do in this hospital to get sedated, I would do it. I wanted that shot. I looked out the window at the vivid blue sky and white tufted clouds, and got an idea.

I began singing the first thing that came into my head in a thin, whispery voice. It was the U.S. Air Force about going into the wild blue yonder. I repeated it, and soon I was floating away. I was floating and flying into the sky.

When I woke up, I was in the Recovery Room. I was too weak to talk. A nurse was pressing on my stomach and I could hear her telling someone else "She's still bleeding." And then she noticed I was awake.

"You're doing great," she said, patting me gently. "Just a little while longer."

I lay there and fell asleep, or I could have passed out. When she came back and woke me and again pressed on my stomach, it felt like I was losing lots of fluid from my vagina. She got very upset.

"She's not okay," I heard her say. "She's hemorrhaging. I have to get a doctor." I heard her leave the room, but everything was fuzzy and out of proportion. I felt strange—light and weak and insubstantial. It felt as if I was unconscious, but I could hear what was happening in the room. I heard the nurse return with a doctor. I heard the doctor confirm that I was hemorrhaging.

"Get everyone ready to go back into the delivery room right away," I heard him say. Then the nurse bent over me and explained what was happening.

"Your husband already left the hospital. Do you want him to come back?"

"Yes, please," I answered weakly. She dialed the number and held the phone to my ear. As I lay on my back on the wheeled gurney, which an orderly was already in position to maneuver through the door, I heard the phone ring three times before Eli answered. I could tell by the half-asleep voice that he had already fallen asleep. I felt angry at how impatient he must have been to leave the hospital and that he hadn't stayed with me to make sure that I was okay.

I can remember the bright lights as they wheeled me into the room and helped to lift me back onto the table. I cooperatively put my feet into the stirrups, which I could see in my mind's eye. The gas again. This time I didn't fight anything. I was relieved to escape this scene. I breathed deeply, and then I was out.

The second time I woke up, I was in my own room, lying in bed, getting a blood transfusion. The nurse came in and told me they were bringing me my baby boy.

"You have a beautiful baby," she said.

Yes, I thought to myself. I have a Mitchell.

As I held him in my arms, I couldn't believe that the delivery was finally over. It was more than I had expected and I was woozy. But I was still alive, despite my mother's frightening warnings. I was alive. I had a new baby. I had Mitchell. As the nurse brought the back of my bed to an upright position, I carefully took the blanket which swaddled my son and watched him wrinkle up his little suntanned face and start to cry. I laughed at his unruly baby hair, black as coal and sticking up in funny tufts, like a Halloween wig. It felt like I had never held a baby before in my life. What a miracle! My son! I created this! I had never been happier in my whole life.

The nurse handed me a warmed bottle of formula. "Hold the head up just a little more," she said. "Try this." As soon as Mitchell sucked in the nipple of the small bottle, the cry disappeared.

"Am I doing this right?" I asked the kind nurse. I couldn't take my eyes off my baby.

"That's perfect," she said.

⁓

Because of the surgery, and more than one hundred stitches, and because I had initially been given a transfusion of the wrong blood type, I was very sick after Mitchell's birth and had to stay in the hospital for over a week. Eli and his family came to visit, as did mine. My mother flew in from California to see me. But these visits didn't cheer or comfort me. I was sore and weak, and I felt as if these visitors, when they did acknowledge me, expected to be entertained. But mostly, all the attention of friends and family was for the baby, the son. I felt invisible. Even Eli, who had left the hospital the night Mitchell was born and hadn't been by my side when I needed to go back for surgery, barely spoke to me except to ask about the baby. I couldn't shake this feeling of resentment. If Eli had watched out for me, maybe I wouldn't have gotten the wrong blood type. It felt as if I existed only to produce this exalted first-born son. I barely got to see my baby, I felt terrible, and there was no one to show me any concern or compassion. Four days after Mitchell's birth, Fred decided we needed to go ahead with the baby's bris even though I was still hospitalized, and my frustration and depression deepened.

In the Jewish religion, it is customary to circumcise boy babies before they are eight days old. This ceremony is performed by a *moyel*, a specially trained expert, usually a rabbi. The *bris* is an important ritual, governed by Jewish law, and also a reason to invite friends and celebrate. Since I could not leave my hospital bed, my father-in-law Fred made the catered affair right at the hospital. To do this, he had to get special permission, which he did. He chose the food, the *moyel* and the guest list. I felt abandoned. I was still too sick for a party, and I couldn't believe it when Fred came into my room and scolded me.

"Get. Up. Get up!" he actually shouted at me. "You have guests to see. Get up!" I could not believe he was expecting me to be a hostess. I was hurting badly from the stitches and I couldn't find a comfortable way to sit. I just wanted to rest and be with my baby. I didn't even want this party. These people were not my friends and family. And my husband was nowhere to be found. He should have been by my side. He should have been protecting me. I tried to refuse.

"I feel weak," I protested. "I'm in pain. I feel sad." But all Fred cared about were the guests. He made me feel so guilty that I got up and put on my bathrobe and slippers. I begrudgingly and gingerly walked out to the reception area, put on a false smile, and said hello to the guests who I had just met once or twice at the engagement party and wedding. There were all kinds of food, but I could not eat. I wasn't hungry. When I got back to my room, I cried quietly.

I was sad. I knew that underneath my aches and fatigue and disappointment, there was a troubling feeling of melancholy, which I didn't understand. I had my baby and he was perfect and I loved him. All of the rest of it—Eli's inattention, his family's arrogance, my family's indifference—had been there before, but I was feeling crushed by sadness. I think I was realizing that nothing was going to change. I had such high hopes that this baby would instigate a new feeling in my families, my marriage and my life. But I saw, during my time in the hospital, that everything was the same. While I was pregnant, I looked forward with anticipation to a new life—Eli, me, and our son, a happy family. I looked forward to belonging and to being valued and loved. After nine months of anticipation, I had the baby, and everything was the same. I still didn't have a marriage. I still didn't matter. Everything was the same.

I was in the hospital for about a week, and then Eli came to take Mitchell and me home. Everything was ready for my baby. I had diapers, clothes, bottles and formula. I had picture books, and I was looking forward to reading my baby to sleep. His nursery was color coordinated. The French provincial highboy twin dressers were red and white. So were the decorated Dorado custom made crib and matching white rocking chair with red and white flowered back and seat pads. The flooring was white and, because I had a boy, I added custom-made blue colored shutters and blue accent pieces. Over Mitchell's head, attached to the crib, hung a musical mobile that played "Lullaby and Good Night," "Mary Had a Little Lamb" and "Three Blind Mice." Mitchell loved it.

Early in my pregnancy, I had reserved a baby nurse, named Claudia, to stay with us for three weeks. She was from Jamaica and came highly recommended; "everybody" used her. But with Claudia I began to understand that what was right for "everybody"—the people of my social, economic and religious circle; Eli's friends and family and co-workers; the "important" people my mother so valued— was not automatically right for me, and hiring her had been a bad choice. Claudia made me profoundly uncomfortable. It was too difficult trying to check and see what she was supposed to do, what she was doing, and if and how she was doing it. She seemed to want to remind me that I knew nothing.

Besides Claudia, there wasn't anyone around to help me to learn how to be a "good" mother and I did not have many mothering skills. Though it is supposed to come naturally, it didn't come naturally for me. I wanted it to. I wanted to talk and share my questions and insecurities. But there weren't any aunts, cousins, sisters-in-law or mother or mother-in-law I could comfortably ask. My sister was still single. My husband worked at least sixty hours a week. So I read all the books and harassed my doctors with questions. I had a lot of information, but no support. I was afraid.

A few days after we came home from the hospital, I left Mitchell with the nurse and went to Bloomingdale's. I was wearing the only outfit I owned that fit me, a navy blue pants suit two sizes larger than I had worn before my pregnancy. I wanted to find other outfits to wear which would be flattering and hide my weight gain. I tried on several outfits but none of them were right. I was remembering the last time I had been in Bloomingdale's, before Mitchell's birth when I had come, armed with my list and my proud, protruding belly. I remembered how happy I had been that day, how pretty I looked and how confident I felt about becoming a mother. That memory seemed to mock me. My body felt heavy and ugly. My baby was at home with a nurse who intimidated me. My husband was at work. And I still had stitches to remind me that the ease with which books described childbirth was, at least in my case, hugely inaccurate. As I was leaving the fitting room, I saw my saleslady and I broke down in tears.

"I just had my first baby," I sobbed, "and I've gained fifteen pounds. I don't fit into any of my clothes." The tears were dripping off my chin, and even though I felt embarrassed, I couldn't seem to stop them. "I cry so much," I whispered, "and I feel so hopeless. I just don't know what to do. I feel like—a wreck." The saleslady was patting my arm gently as I continued. "I'm so fat and it still hurts to walk—from the stitches—and I can't sleep." I was in full-blown sob now, my makeup smeared and my nose running.

She was such a nice person. She put her arm around me. "You know, hon," she said, "that's called the baby blues; that's post-partum depression." It was the first time I had ever heard that term. The books didn't talk about it and I could identify the feelings although I was in denial. I didn't want to have anything wrong with me. I wanted my old body back. I wanted that nurse out of my house. I wanted a mother, or a husband, or a sister to put an arm around me and comfort me, not a saleswoman at Bloomingdale's. I wanted to not hurt anymore. I wanted to love my son completely and joyfully. I wanted to get some sleep.

⁓

When Mitchell was four weeks old, I decided to take him out to the park in his new, one-piece navy top-of-the-line Marmet large baby carriage. I was finally feeling less sore, and I wanted to go out with my baby. I was eager to go "public" with my new persona: the pretty young mother, the Upper East Side Mom like the ones I had so admired.

Claudia and I dressed Mitchell up in a new outfit with closed feet along with the hand-knitted yellow and white blanket with matching booties and bonnet made by Aunt Ruth, my mother's sister in Los Angeles. It was a lovely summer day. I picked up the mail in the lobby and pushed the carriage across the street towards a small park on the East River at the end of Fifty-seventh Street. I found an empty bench and sat down. Mitchell had miraculously fallen asleep. So, I opened the mail. Nothing very important.

And I sat there. *What now?* I thought. *Do I just sit here on the bench and watch Mitchell sleep?* I sorted through the mail again, smoothed the skirt of my pretty summer dress, looked around me, checked on Mitchell, who hadn't moved since the last time I checked him a minute before.

I stood up and walked home. I hadn't thought about what one did after the baby and the cute outfit and the summer day and the top-of-the-line carriage. I hadn't thought about what a mother did once she got to that park bench. In my mind I had created motherhood as an image, not a series of actions. I didn't know what to do once the image had been realized.

I pushed the carriage home feeling empty. I didn't know anything about motherhood. Back in the apartment, I put Mitchell in his crib and I got back into my bed. *I'm just not a park bench mother*, I thought, but I didn't know what kind of mother I was. I was depressed. I wanted to talk to someone but nobody was there.

⌒∽

I was having a love affair with my new son, Mitchell. I kissed and held him, fed him and changed his diapers morning, noon and night. He was very much visible and audible. Although I gave him practically all of my time and energy, it seemed as if he cried a lot of the time, most of the time.

My baby doctor was a wonderful stout woman, Dr. Cynthia Hall, whose office was on Park Avenue. She was recommended to me and I saw her as an experienced motherly replacement. Although I asked a lot of questions, I still felt ashamed to reveal how inadequate and frustrated I really felt about everything I should know how to do with Mitchell.

As soon as I brought him home from the hospital, I was anxious about his constant crying and moving. He never seemed to stop moving. He was always crawling up to the head of his crib and when he got there, he would keep moving the top of his head into the foam rubber bumpers, non-stop. Thank God for those bumpers! I would move him to the middle of the crib and back he would go, up to the bumpers, moving as fast as he could. Whether he was crying or not, I would get up compulsively during the night to see if possibly the diaper pins had opened up by mistake as a result of all of his thrashing and moving about. Those big diaper pins, even with the safety catch, provoked a sense of danger in me.

Dr. Hall told me Mitchell was a "hyperactive" baby and if and when I felt it necessary, it would not hurt to add one-half of a baby aspirin into his applesauce. I was also given a prescription for some kind of drops to help him to sleep. Since I've always been adverse to most medications, I only used them twice, preferring to hear the crying rather than medicating my baby. Dr. Hall also told me that Mitchell had colic and that's why he cried so much. *Just hold him*, she said. *It's what he wants.* So, I held him. I patted him on the back a great deal. I walked around and around with him on my shoulder. He did love the movement. I felt so triumphant when I finally was able to get him to burp.

That didn't come quick. Sometimes, it took more than ten minutes of patting him on the back to get him to burp, but it was worth it. Because that meant that now he would probably sleep through the night. So I did a lot of that. When Eli was at home, he tried to help and also walked around with a diaper and Mitchell on his shoulder.

Mitchell became a very expressive baby, and it was easy to get him to smile. He truly was a happy baby and brought a great deal of joy into my life. I can well remember Mitchell's first bath, which took place on the dining room table. I was nervous that I wouldn't do it right, so Eli and I did it together. Mitchell was in awe of the water and seemed to love every second.

When Mitchell got big enough, I lowered him into the seat of the feeding table. How he enjoyed putting his hands into the food, if he could get it, and smushing it all over the top of the table. I remember the one time that my father tried to feed him. I was not in the room and Mitchell got a hold of the feeding dish and dumped his food all over the table and floor. I laughed when I saw the mess. He was my joy.

Mitchell was definitely not a boring baby and I got the biggest kick out of him. We definitely were bonded. He knew who I was. I was his Mommy.

Ironically, the strongest guide I had for making decisions about how to mother my son came from my own mother, and it was parenting by opposition. Being with my little boy invariably led me to memories of my own girlhood, and I was determined that my son would never feel put down or unimportant; I was determined to raise a child who believed in himself, who felt loved and wanted and confident. Even when Mitchell would cry, I welcomed the noise, and later, when he started to babble, and then speak words and sentences, I conversed with him as if those noises and fractured phrases were the most profound thoughts I had ever heard. Modeling my delivery on Muhammad Ali, who was at the height of his career during Mitchell's early childhood, I'd say:

> *Mitchell, you are the greatest.*
> *You're the greatest.*
> *You can do anything you want.*
> *Always remember that.*

I would make him repeat it after me, and I have a clear memory of my son standing in his crib, laughing at his mother as she danced in front of him crowing *You're the greatest! Repeat after me. . . .* And he would, mangling the words in toddler talk, but repeating just the same.

Later, when Mitchell excelled in school—top of his class academically; starting player on every team; Ivy League undergraduate and law school—I would think about those early days with something like pride; it seemed that, despite all the dysfunction in our family and the ways Mitchell would suffer from it, one thing at least stayed with him: that he was great; that he could do anything.

I got him into one of the best nursery schools in the city and all seemed to go well for us there. I was active with the Parent Teacher Association, and it turned out to be an excellent choice. During the summers, we did different things. One summer we rented a car and I drove to a beach club in Westchester every day with Mitchell sitting in a car seat in the back. He was a happy, bubbling toddler. He loved the car seat. He loved any activity we did together. I talked a lot to Mitchell not only during the drive to and from the club but during the day as well. I would teach him songs and I praised him all the time. I wanted him to feel special. I knew it was important for him to feel loved and well taken care of. I tried to teach Mitchell to excel and he did. I kissed him a lot. I was so very proud of him and I still am.

When Mitchell turned two, we were summering on Nantucket and my friend Marianne had come up to visit with her husband. I hadn't planned an official "party" for Mitchell, but we were going to have a nice birthday dinner and cake and a piñata. My special touch, though, was that I had made us matching outfits. Using royal blue fabric with red and white poppies, I made Mitchell overalls, and a pants suit for myself. As always, my little boy was bubbling with pleasure at any activity we could do together. I wasn't sure he really understood that he and Mommy were dressed the same, but I thought we looked cute. Anything I did with my son gave both of us immense pleasure.

During these growing up years, Mitchell and I were very close. When Mitchell turned five, I made him a big birthday party with about twenty of his friends and their mothers at The Cattleman, a restaurant in the West Forties. There was a clown lady who made balloon animals. Mitchell got lots of birthday presents but the one that he loved the best was a very large, shiny red fire engine. He wouldn't put it down. After the party was over and we came home, we went out to play. Mitchell took the fire engine and we walked over to the East River Drive, along the water. A little boy who was a couple of years younger than Mitchell was there with his nanny and spied the shiny red fire engine. He wanted to take it but Mitchell didn't want to let it go.

"Mitchell," I said. "You need to share with him. Let him play with it for a little while." I wanted to teach my son to be generous. I thought it was important that he learn values like sharing. After all, he would have a brother or sister someday. I wanted my son to be a *good* person.

Mitchell didn't want to let go of his new toy, but he was such an obedient and trusting little boy, he did as I asked.

The other boy took the big fire engine over to the water. He placed it on top of the railing. His nanny wasn't close enough or watching, and we were too far away. In an instant, the new big, red shiny fire engine fell into the East River.

Mitchell cried hysterically and I felt hysterical as well. The nanny apologized. The other little boy and Mitchell were crying. We came home feeling so upset. What was supposed to be a day of a happy celebration ended with this disappointment and, for Mitchell at five, genuine grief. I don't think Mitchell or I will ever forget that day.

Since then, I've always felt guilty about this incident. I've tried to make it up to Mitchell over the years with other fire engines but I've always known that I could never replace what he lost that day—not only the fire engine, but his sense of the world as a gentle place.

∞

When Mitchell was about two-and-a-half months old, my father had to have one of the first experimental open heart surgeries at New York Hospital. It was a very serious operation, and Sandra and I didn't want him left alone in his room post-surgery. We were able to hire private duty nurses to stay with him, and I was able to find babysitters for Mitchell so that I could visit for long stretches every day. About a week after the surgery, I went to New York Hospital as usual, to visit my father. I stayed for several hours and had planned my day so that I could go downtown and visit Eli at the office.

I rarely stopped by my husband's law firm, but it was a warm early fall afternoon, and I was dressed to go out. In those days, the good Upper East Side wife dressed to go places; there was no such thing as wearing jeans, and tracksuits were an unimaginable fashion horror. Anytime I left my apartment, it was in full makeup, wearing an "outfit" which, more often than not, included matching bag and shoes. On the day I left my father at the hospital and headed towards Eli's office, I was wearing an emerald green, short sleeved linen A-line dress with white accent around the collar and the cuffs, with white heels and bag to match. I looked very stylish, I thought, and didn't want to waste it. Visiting Eli gave me a place to go. I held onto the hope that maybe he'd enjoy seeing me. I was still trying to connect with him. I was still trying to be part of my husband's life.

I took a taxi to midtown and decided to walk a couple of blocks before going indoors again. As I walked past a costume jewelry store on Fifth Avenue & Forty-second Street, I went in just to see what was there. I remember that the first counter was of no interest and when I got to the next one, I heard a pleasant voice asking if I needed any help.

I looked up with a smile, prepared to say "No thank you, just browsing" and found myself face- to-face with Lila Kinsler, my ex-boyfriend Alex's mother. I hadn't seen her in five years, but she still had sparkling honest eyes, a pretty mouth and a fair white complexion. It was a face that I liked and I thought was pretty the moment I first met her. You had to love her open, up attitude. I felt happy to see her.

"I don't believe it!" I cried. "It's me," I said with a wide smile, "Myrna Kaye. Do you remember me?"

"Of course," she answered, squeezing my hand. "How good to see you! You look terrific. How are you?" She was the kind of person who seemed genuinely interested in the answer, and I was remembering how much I had enjoyed being with her and the rest of Alex's family.

"Well," I said. "It's Kramer now." I smiled and gestured toward my left hand. "I got married."

"That's so good to hear," she told me. "Congratulations!"

"We live on Fifty-seventh Street and Sutton Place," I continued. "My husband is a lawyer and I have a baby boy." Lila smiled when she heard about my son. "His name is Mitchell," I told her. "He's almost three months old."

As I was talking, I made a gesture to fix the front of my hair so that she would notice the large pear-shaped engagement ring flashing on my left hand. Although she did nothing to inspire it, I felt inadequate somehow; guilty maybe. For the two years that her son and I had been involved, this woman had been nothing but gracious and welcoming to me. And when Alex and I broke up, the suddenness of it meant that I never had a chance to thank her or say goodbye. I was afraid she thought badly of me, and I didn't know how to explain. All I could think of to do was to impress her with my big ring and my lawyer husband, hoping this would make her think I was a very important and worthy person. At that point in my life, it was a lot of the self image I had; that and my looks. I thought to myself *thank goodness I look good today*. I mentally checked that I had just put on fresh lipstick so I looked okay.

Lila didn't seem to notice my ring, and I felt like she was actually listening to me, not evaluating my appearance. "What brings you to this neighborhood?" she asked.

"I'm on my way to see my husband at his office," I explained. "I just left my father at New York Hospital." She looked concerned. "He had open heart surgery a few days ago." I paused, feeling a little awkward sharing such personal information. "I feel anxious about it," I finally concluded.

"I'm sorry to hear about your father," she said sincerely. "I hope he'll be fine. Please tell him we send him our best."

"I will," I said. "Thank you." I felt so grateful for her concern. Seeing her again made me remember how much I respected this woman. She truly liked herself and it was reflected in all of her attitudes and mannerisms. She was a happy and satisfied person even though she was working behind the counter in a costume (not even real) jewelry store. If the situation had been reversed and I was working here and she had come in as a customer, I knew I would probably have felt embarrassed. But she seemed completely comfortable and pleased to see me. Not for an instant did she feel or look jealous when I flashed my ring. I felt so ashamed. If you put my life next to hers, I thought, hers was richer and more meaningful. I looked at her cheerful face, and the memories of Alex washed over me. I wondered if I could ask her about him. But then she decided for me.

"I'm so glad you found someone, Myrna," she said. "Sonny was engaged, but it didn't work out." I smiled, hearing her call her son by the nickname I never used, although it was very fitting. Alex was such a cheerful, fun-loving boy when I knew him. But then I realized it might look as if I was smiling at the broken engagement. I adjusted my features.

"That's too bad for him," I said. "I hope he's getting over it."

"Oh yes," she said. "Now he's engaged to another girl. He lives near you on Fiftieth Street between First and Second."

My heart flip-flopped. I tried hard not to show any feeling in my face but I don't know if I was successful. He lived less than a dozen blocks from me and wasn't yet married. I was thinking that maybe I would run into him; maybe this long-lost friend, my first and only real boyfriend, could be back in my life, after five years. I wouldn't have admitted to anyone how often I thought of Alex; almost every day and night, wondering what had happened to him.

I was hurting badly; I didn't want to see Eli. I wanted to stay here with this kind woman, who felt more accepting of me than my own mother. I looked at her. She looked wise. She had such unconditional loving energy.

"Well, I've got to be on my way," I finally said. "I'm late and Eli is waiting for me."

I visited Eli. As usual, there wasn't any emotional exchange or satisfaction. It felt like a medical visit to a strange doctor, without any connection one way or the other.

When I got home that afternoon, I sat at the dining room table, lost in thought. My eyes kept straying to the wall phone in the kitchen. I felt drawn to it. I thought about what I had, and what I wanted.

What I had was an empty marriage. Eli was rarely at home. I ate dinner alone after a day of taking care of the house, shopping, cooking, tending to Mitchell, doing light cleaning, laundry, and all the rest. Once a week, I had a cleaning girl who I could also leave Mitchell with so I could go shopping. My friend Ann was my only regular adult company. She often joined Mitchell and me for dinner; after Eli would call and tell me he was going to be late. I hated eating dinner alone.

My feelings were badly hurting; Eli didn't ask, didn't care and didn't know about how I felt or what I wanted. And I did the same with him. We were like two strangers sharing the same bed, same house, same child. But that was all we had. About that time, the song about meeting a stranger in the night was popular. Every time I heard it I wanted to cry. It seemed to describe Eli and me, except that we were strangers in the night, strangers in the day, and strangers all the way. Were there other marriages as bad as mine? Perhaps some were worse. But, probably most of them were better. Or at least the woman had other people around who cared for her and supported her.

As I sat at the table thinking, I remembered a night when Eli and I were in bed, watching television. It was a Sunday evening and we were watching *The Ed Sullivan*

Show, when a singer came on and did a song called "How To Handle A Woman." The last line was that the only way to deal with a woman was to just love her. I felt so moved by this performance and as I looked over at Eli, I hoped that he got it. But I knew, with resignation, that he didn't. There was no acknowledgment from him. Eli was not emotional, or demonstrative, and he didn't like music. He was the exact opposite of Alex, who had sung and danced and kissed me and told me all the time that he loved me. I stared at the phone. I wanted to see Alex.

Because I'd been happy with him.

I walked to the telephone. I picked up the receiver. I dialed information.

"Operator, I want the address and telephone number of. . . ." I paused. I was nervous. "The name is either Alex or Alexander Kinsler, on East Fiftieth Street, between First and Second Avenues."

In what felt like two seconds, she said "Alexander" and spit out a number.

Shocked that she had it, I wrote it down just as quickly. I hung up the receiver. I immediately dialed the telephone number. The phone rang twice. A loud, deep voice answered.

"Hello."

I knew it was his voice.

"Hello," I said, my voice trembling slightly.

"I love you," he said.

CHAPTER EIGHT

It was 1957. We were living in a second-floor apartment on Argyle Road, between Church Avenue and Caton Avenue, in the Flatbush section of Brooklyn. There was a small elevator, but I usually walked up the stairs.

My sister Sandra and I shared a bedroom with two twin beds and a dressing room table. There were bedspreads with matching curtains on both windows, frilled covers for the pillows and a skirt for the dressing room table in a fresh blue flowered pattern; my mother always made sure that we had a dressing room table. She thought it was a necessity for a girl to learn how to sit down and comb her hair like a lady. We also had two windows and a large closet. The front window looked out on Argyle Road. From that window I could see the big apartment building across the street with the trees in front of it. From the smaller window, next to my bed, I could see the courtyard in front of our smaller building. We had a twin building next door, just across the street from the parade grounds in Prospect Park.

My good friend Janet, a senior with me at the Riverside School, was dating a guy who had a friend named

Alexander Kinsler, who lived in Flatbush, Brooklyn. Janet wanted to fix us up, so a blind date was arranged. Since I had attended school out of town, I really didn't know anyone in the neighborhood and I had nothing better to do. I had just graduated from Riverside after spending only one year there and now planning to go away to Bennington College in Vermont within a couple of weeks. I had picked this school because while I was growing up, we used to go to Vermont to visit my grandparents who lived on Cranberry Street in Bennington. I remembered it as feeling like walking into another time and place. I even watched the iceman deliver the huge solid piece of ice for their icebox and watched them put it inside, down at the bottom of the box. My grandmother had a huge, twelve-burner stove, an oversized radio and a Victrola in the living room. We called her "the General" because she managed her family like a battalion of reluctant foot soldiers. Everyone had a job, and she was the one who dished them out. Mine was to sweep the sidewalks around her house.

I felt like I wanted to hold onto this piece of my roots and also my identity. I wanted to live someplace simpler than New York City. And I loved the greenery and the scenery of Vermont.

It was close to the end of August, 1957, the tail end of the summer, and I couldn't wait to leave for college. The time couldn't pass fast enough. So when Alex Kinsler called me on the telephone, I decided to meet him. We made a casual plan. Since he lived on Ocean Avenue, near Sutter's Bakery and the Church Avenue subway, and it wasn't too far from my house on Argyle Road, he could walk over and pick me up.

I can remember that when he got there and I opened the front door, I was impressed. I was in awe of his height. I hadn't really thought about what six-two looked like. He had big broad shoulders. He looked powerful. He walked right into the living room and in an instant I thought *Wow, he's really tall. But he's not too tall for me.* I loved that height. In fact, I was very impressed by the way he walked straight into our living room, making himself right at home, and seeming to fill the room with a masculinity I had had no previous experience of. I was immediately attracted.

"Hi, my name is Sonny," he said, punctuating his introduction with his beaming smile. I made a little face at the nickname.

"Sonny?" I asked. "I thought your name was Alex."

"My friends all call me Sonny," he answered. "You can call me Alex if you want. Or Sonny."

"Well, Sonny doesn't sound like a real name." I said, rather primly. "I like the name Alex. I choose Alex."

With a big open gesture and that sunbeam smile, he touched my shoulder and said, "Sure. Whatever you like." Even that small touch made me shiver.

We hadn't made any specific plans, so when Alex suggested we go for a walk, I thought that sounded fine. We walked along Argyle Road and up Church Avenue, past bustling shops and families with the same idea as ours. On the way, Alex asked me if it was all right if we walked to his house. He'd like to take me home and introduce me to his parents. I agreed. But when we got to his house, no one was home.

"Would you like to dance?" he asked, as we stood in the living room of the neat, quiet apartment.

"Yes," I answered. I loved to dance.

Alex gave me a choice of a couple of different records. He flipped through the family's music collection, pulling out a selection of square cardboard covers each containing a heavy black vinyl disc in a special manila-colored dust jacket. I was surprised to find classical music among the choices he offered me. I didn't expect that he would like that kind of music. It appeared to me that this family enjoyed music together, and I tried to imagine my family doing that, sharing the pleasures of classical music, and I couldn't. My mother was gone for good, my father was gone most of the time and Sandra and I couldn't seem to get past our endless competition for the little parental attention there was left. I didn't even like thinking about it, especially just then. I knew so few truly happy people. I wanted to absorb some of this boy's warmth while I could. I turned to him with a smile and picked up one of the albums he had pulled down from the shelf. "You choose," I said. He just seemed to know better than me.

Alex picked his favorite—a romantic instrumental called "Grand Canyon Suite"— and put it onto the turntable of the large standing record player, a heavy machine inside a dark stained wooden cabinet. As soon as he put one arm on my shoulder and the other arm around me, I felt a spark. A special chemistry. I had to reach up, and I liked that feeling. Alex started to hum along with the music. Another surprise—it sounded like he had a good singing voice. My eyes closed as I danced with him. I was transported into a land of happiness, music and song. It was easy to follow him. I didn't have to take huge steps either. He was a good dancer, moved well and was a good leader. We danced well together.

We were interrupted when his parents came in. As they stepped into the foyer, we were dancing right in front of them. I stopped the moment I heard them, and Alex introduced me. For some reason, I felt guilty to have been "caught" dancing, but I liked them. Alex's father was not as tall as he was and had a definite stomach revealed by his tee shirt. I thought his mother was pretty. She had dark hair, like me, with a smooth white complexion. She was more outgoing than his father and welcomed me into their home with sincerity. I felt good there in that house. We all chatted for a few minutes, and we were encouraged to go back to dancing.

Immediately, I felt like part of the family. We went back to dancing together in the sunken living room. It should have felt funny to be dancing in a strange home with a new friend; I should have felt inhibited that his parents were around. But it didn't. I felt like I was right where I belonged.

Alex's parents were going to have dessert and called us from the living room to join them. The four of us sat at their glass-top dining room table. Alex drank a glass of milk. We talked, and I remember hearing about the time that the glass top had been broken and how expensive it was to replace it. We laughed a lot. They accepted me and they were interested in me. They made me feel appreciated, and in turn I liked and appreciated them.

When it was time to go home I said good night to Alex's parents and followed him down to the street. It was such a pretty summer night and as we walked home, I knew that I really liked this boy. He acted like he really liked me. When we got to my house, I turned to say goodbye to him and he kissed me.

I was so surprised. I couldn't believe this boy was kissing me when we had just met, and so passionately. I was trembling, part from fear of discovery—we were right outside my front door—and partly because Alex's kisses were making me feel weak and hot and almost liquid; like I had no power to resist him because some newly awakened part of me didn't want to. I knew what my mother would say: this boy was low class.

I kissed Alex back.

When he broke the long, wet kiss, I gasped for breath. I was leaning against his hard chest, encircled in his arms. He bent to my ear.

"I have to go to the bathroom," he whispered. "Can I please come in?"

"I think my father is sleeping," I said.

He screwed his face up as if he were in pain. But his eyes were sparkling and, as I looked up into his face, he seemed to be holding back a smile.

"I really need to go," he said in a wheedling voice. "Please. I'll be very quiet."

So I let him into the living room and showed him where the bathroom was.

When he came out, he did not go for the front door. He put his arms around me and we started kissing. I don't remember what I was thinking but I didn't check my feelings as I usually did. He had a big tongue and really kissed well, and his lips and tongue were soft and juicy. I didn't want to stop, but finally, when I thought I heard my father in the bedroom, I pulled away.

"I—I have to get up early," I said the first thing that came to mind as I tried to regain my composure. "Thank you for a—lovely evening."

Alex was looking down at me with an amused grin. He still hadn't released me from his embrace. I wiggled a little against him, not really trying to get free.

"You know," he growled, bending so his lips were at my ear, his warm breath raising goose bumps on my arms, "I gotta have a glass of milk."

I giggled. "You just had cake and about a gallon. Why do you need more milk?"

"Because I got blue balls. Milk cures blue balls."

"What are blue balls?" I asked. I had no idea.

"When a guy needs to have an orgasm and can't," he answered. I barely suppressed my gasp. I couldn't believe he had just said that. I think it was the first time, except for late-night discussions with my girlfriends, that I had ever heard the word "orgasm" spoken out loud, and certainly never by a boy I had just kissed. I was so embarrassed that I didn't know what to say.

"Milk? Cures blue—balls?" I finally stammered. Alex's arms tightened around my waist and he pulled me hard against him. "Some milk could cure me," he whispered in a silky voice. "But I'd rather have some of you."

I think I heard him laughing as he walked away from me toward the stairs. I was already looking forward to seeing him again.

I felt very happy when I got into bed that night. Imagine that! This guy Alex takes me home to his house on the first date to introduce me to his parents. I thought he must have liked me a lot. I liked his house and his parents. They seemed like a real bonded family, and I didn't know any families like that. The friends I had gone to Riverside School with during the past year were all from broken homes; their parents were divorced, like mine. Alex's family wasn't rich, I knew, but I thought they were happy, alive and connected. I wanted to feel those things, and as I lay there thinking, a sense of possibility bloomed inside me. Maybe I could feel them with this boy.

I thought about his odd parting sally: blue balls! What in the world could that feel like? I thought it was one of those mysterious and dangerous things about men that my mother had always alluded to but never explained. I knew he shouldn't have said that to me, but the truth was I liked that he had. I liked that he talked out loud about those whispered "dirty" things girls were always warned about. It was the first of many times that my relationship with Alex would challenge a value I thought I believed in; the first of many times I would "split." Part of me primly decided this boy was rude. He didn't know how to treat a nice girl. But another part of me, a part I knew far less well, thought I had finally met someone who was comfortably open and honest.

I knew I had made Alex feel something passionate. It was my first real experience with male desire and I liked it: I liked inspiring it and I liked talking about it and I knew I shouldn't like either of those things.

I closed my eyes and lost myself in the memory of Alex's kisses and the heat of his body as he held me. I could hear Sandra's breathing, deep and regular, in the other twin bed as I trailed my hand gently down my body, caressing myself as I thought of Alex, needing to ease the ache he had inspired in me. What was that ache called, I wondered. There was a word for this feeling in a man—*blue balls*—but what was it called in me?

When I think back on it now, on the ways that girls in the fifties were expected to deny their bodies and hide the fact that they had sexual feelings, this residual Victorianism seems foolish. But at the time, it was anything but. It was deadly serious and so much a part of my outlook that my English teacher at the Riverside School had once told me that I wrote with too much "Victorian bias." I didn't know what that meant. I wasn't yet able to distinguish between myself as an individual, and the values of the collective from which I had sprung. Girls were taught that *husbands* would be our protectors, but that *men* were predators; they couldn't help it. They had urges. They had *needs*, and they would try to get us to satisfy those needs. Because they were men. We should expect to have to defend ourselves, just as they expected to put us in that defensive position. It was a sick little dance, but no one questioned it. And those girls who refused the dance, who gave in to the pressures of boys, who *participated*, were the "bad" ones. They were considered weak or desperate or of questionable morality. No one ever imagined that bad girls were bad because they just couldn't fight anymore; and no one ever imagined that some girls simply liked it; liked to be intimate and physical with men. No one ever imagined that girls could have blue balls too.

The consequence for me, and for many other girls, I'm sure, is that I was at war with my body; constantly craving stimulation, hungry for touch while at the same time denying those feelings or carrying the burden of guilt when I indulged them.

I loved the feelings I had when Alex kissed me. I loved how he pressed my body so tightly against his. I loved hearing him sing those beautiful songs in my ear while I was dancing with him.

During the next couple of weeks, I saw a lot of Alex before we both left for our freshman year of college—he to Austin and me to Bennington. He was planning to drive all the way to Texas in his small black car. We said goodbye affectionately, promised to write and planned to see each other on vacations. I'm not sure whether Alex would have wanted to go "steady" after dating for such a short time, and studying at schools so far from each other, but I knew I didn't. I wanted freedom and new experiences. I had such high hopes for what my life could be in Bennington, and I didn't want to be tied to a boy so far away. Still, he had made the summer memorable and I knew that, no matter what happened between us, Alex was special.

He wrote only a few letters: short and dry, and I remember he printed rather than wrote cursive, which I thought was juvenile but kind of funny. He took me out over school breaks, but our breaks did not always coincide and he often had many family obligations. Still, we saw each other enough for our attachment to grow, although I never allowed myself to admit how strong my feelings were for him. I only knew that when I was with Alex I felt happier, more comfortable and more loved than I ever had before. And I had more fun.

We went out to dinner and for walks and to the beach when the weather was fine. He took me to the horse races, which was a first for me but not for him. I found out that he used to go on a regular basis with his family. He and his parents would go for their regular outing on a Sunday in their big Cadillac, sometimes joined by his sister. They went as a family, to be together, the way other families might go to worship. But this was worship of a different kind. Instead of going to church on Sunday to pray together, this family went to the track and placed their bets together. This activity felt wrong and sleazy to me. I heard from Alex that his father was a real big gambler. Sometimes they were rich and sometimes they didn't have enough money to pay the rent. Sometimes, Alex confided in me, his mother didn't even have grocery money. Everyone suffered when funds were low. It bothered Alex, I know, which is why he told me in the first place.

It bothered me too. I made a mental note. I filed this information under "important;" it seemed to be some kind of red flag: *Do not ever marry a gambler. You will never have comfort and security.* I wanted comfort and security; I wanted peace, home, family, a place in the community—all the things I'd never had. Alex was so different, so nonchalant about things. We talked all the time, but my enjoyment of our conversations was often disrupted, despite my attempts to banish it, by my mother's voice, complaining about the "low class" Brooklyn accent she heard in the speech of every neighbor we ever had. "Kikes!" she would snap, "Low-class Brooklyn Jews" accompanied by a dismissive wave of her hand. Had my mother been around, she would have, after one minute of hearing Alex speak, dismissed him with that same gesture. Sometimes I was mortified by the thought of my mother ever meeting him.

And so the only logical conclusion to draw from this story Alex had shared about his father's gambling habits was that I should never consider seriously making a life with him. Alex liked to gamble, like his father. He couldn't offer me what I thought I wanted most. This information influenced the rest of my life.

Don't fall in love with Alex, I told myself. But the fact of the matter was that I already had. I just didn't know it.

My fears—of instability, of being disrespected, of giving into desire and therefore giving away my reputation as a "good" girl—left me perpetually torn. I wanted to be with Alex all the time, but I felt I shouldn't. I wanted to be brave, unique, an innovator. I wanted to disdain convention, social constrictions, my mother's warped values, and make a choice that was right for me regardless of what my family and community thought. But another part of me was so afraid of being different or conspicuous or labeled frivolous; that part wanted to be compliant and just like every one else; that part wanted to disappear into the crowd, where it was safe.

Still, I couldn't stay away from that boy. Sometimes, in unguarded moments when I could think clearly about my relationship with Alex, I would remember a night early on; it might have been our second or third date. We were on the couch at his house, kissing and hugging, and I was stroking his back. It was warm and he wasn't wearing a shirt. As my hand caressed his bare skin, I experienced such a magnetic draw that I felt how much I loved him. In an instant, I was overwhelmed. The idea of lifting my hand from his firm, warm flesh, of denying myself the feeling of his rippling muscles beneath my fingers, felt impossible. I didn't ever want to stop touching him. It was so frightening. I felt lost. It felt like drowning, like I could lose myself, lose Myrna, in this feeling. It felt like death, or like the purest expression of being alive, and it terrified me. If this be love. . . .

I had no preparation whatsoever to deal with the emotional and sexual feelings which Alex inspired in me. I buried them as deep as I could. I told myself *This connection is just physical* and therefore not to be taken seriously. I told myself the powerful attraction I felt to Alex was bad. My training had dictated that I was not supposed to feel, and I really was not capable of handling strong emotion. All these feelings were simmering in a tightly lidded soup pot, getting hotter and thicker as they heated up toward a boil.

Alex and I were dating in a very meaningful way. We made out all the time. We liked to neck and pet, but only above the waist. Even that really wasn't allowed but I decided above the waist was as far as I would go. Nothing else would be permitted. In fact, I felt as if I was already crossing the correct boundary and it took all my energy to keep Alex from advancing further. He wanted to have sex with me so badly he would beg and whine and try to nudge me forward in stages: *Just be next to me,* he would whisper when I tried to slow him down. We would both be naked from the waist up, and he would drive me wild by teasing my nipples. I loved that so much. I would be lost in sensation, usually coming back to myself just in time to stop him from lifting my skirt. *Just be next to me.*

One night, during our winter break in January, 1959, Alex and I were seated in his small black car, parked right in front of my apartment house, when he took a white box out of his pocket. His face was lit by childlike delight. He loved to give presents.

"Surprise!" he said as he handed it to me. I was confused. It wasn't my birthday.

"What's this for?" I asked as I accepted the tiny box.

"Because you're going away," Alex answered. "Don't want you to forget about me when you get back to school."

I was so pleased. I hadn't expected anything. We were both broke college students. I took the box from him and untied the ribbon. Inside the box was

a very shiny flowery engraved heart. I picked it up. It was a fourteen-carat gold locket on a chain. My eyes filled with tears. I was so touched.

"Oh, Alex," I turned to him. "This must have been expensive."

"Don't worry about that," he said, smiling as he looked at the jewelry. I loved how much pleasure Alex took from giving presents. I think he was happier giving them than getting them. "The locket opens," he said. "Open it up."

When I did, I saw that he had put a picture of himself and a picture of me in this two-sided locket. "It's beautiful," I said softly. "I'll wear this locket all the time."

"Let me put it on for you," Alex said, taking the necklace gently from my hand and unhooking the clasp. His hands were warm against my neck, caressing me as he lifted my hair from my neck and slipped the chain around it.

"I will never take this off," I whispered. "I love you." It was the first time I'd ever said those words to Alex or anyone outside of my family. I didn't know whether they were true.

As ironic as it sounds now, I didn't know how to recognize love. I could recognize Alex as inappropriate for any number of reasons, and believed this inappropriateness precluded authentic love. I said "I love you" to Alex that wintry day because I hadn't gotten him a present. The fact that I did love him, that in reality I was telling the truth and didn't even know it, would not become apparent to me until years later.

Alex fastened the catch on the chain. We kissed. It was one of those big juicy soul kisses with his big tongue. When we stopped to breathe, Alex told me he loved me too.

❧

It was the end of June and summer was here, the summer after our sophomore year of college. We were both in Brooklyn at home. Alex was taking a summer class at New York University. I can remember how he couldn't and didn't pay attention in class. He didn't know how to take good notes. So I went to class with him and tried to help him by taking some notes for him. After class, we drove back to Brooklyn in his car. It was one of the first hot, summer days.

We wound up back at his house. The plan was that he would put on his bathing suit so we could go to the beach. But, somehow, we wound up in his parents' bedroom. I think he said he couldn't find his bathing suit and went in there to look for it. No one was home and I was waiting for him down the hall, in the living room. I heard him call me.

"I can't find it," he shouted. "Come here. It's cooler in here."

I thought that it probably wasn't, even though there was a window air conditioner. But I figured he wanted me to help him look for the bathing suit and I didn't want to say so. I walked down the hall and found Alex, shirtless, in his parents' bedroom. I looked at him and smiled. He looked so handsome: guileless but sexy. There was a basket of laundry next to the bed and I crossed the room, prepared to search through it for Alex's suit. As I stepped to within his reach, he grasped my arm and pulled me to him. I didn't resist.

I could feel his hands on my behind, stroking me as he swept his tongue through my willing mouth. Because of the difference in our heights, he had this way of bending my head far back so that if I opened my eyes, I'd be looking at the ceiling, and he kissed with such concentration. He could make me melt with his lips and tongue, and I was melting then. The room was getting hotter and hotter. Alex had pulled my sleeveless blouse free of the waistband of my shorts and was expertly opening the buttons and sliding it off my shoulders without ever breaking the kiss. I could feel the cool air on my bare back, and then I could feel his fingers unhooking my bra, and then pushing down my shorts until they pooled around my ankles. He broke the kiss and nudged me towards the bed.

Lay down he whispered. *It's okay. Lay down.* I watched from the bed as he took off his own shorts, and put my arms out when he lowered himself next to me.

We were laying together in a tangle of bare limbs, kissing and stroking each other. This was the closest we had ever been to being naked together; always before there was clothing unfastened and shifted, his pants unbuttoned as he tried with typical determination to guide my hand down there; my blouse flapping open, bra unfastened and up beneath my chin, or halfway down my arms, pinning them to my sides. I thought how nice and cool and comfortable it felt to be lying there with Alex. I felt perfectly safe. My panties were still on, as were his briefs, and for some reason I believed that thin cotton barrier was my protection. Alex started playing with my nipples and I arched my back and moaned.

"Good," he said. "*Nice.*" But I couldn't think of what he meant.

"Touch it," he said, grasping my wrist and placing my hand on his erection. I started to get scared. I had never realized the sheer size of it; I had never realized that a "hard-on" was literally that: rock hard, long and thick. I struggled to sit up.

"We have to stop."

"No. *Please.*" He was struggling out of his briefs and I froze. I couldn't take my eyes off his penis. I'd never seen one before. I thought it was beautiful and horrible and I momentarily forgot that I was in his parents' bed with him. Until I felt his hand jerking my panties down.

He rolled over, pinning me to the mattress and I pushed against him. "*No, Alex,*" I said softly. "*No.*" I trusted him. We had been petting from the waist up, but not like this . . . on his parents' bed! Always before, Alex had stopped when I asked him to. Yes, he always stopped, and I told myself that he would stop.

I did know that he was on top of me. His weight was hurting me. I tried to move but I was completely pinned down by the size and the weight of his body. My God, I was in a hold. He was holding me down against my will. I couldn't believe it, and because what was happening was so bizarre to me, so inexplicable, I denied it in a weird internal dialogue with myself: *I don't know what's going on. I know what's going on, and it's very bad. This can't be happening. This is happening. He'll stop when he realizes he's hurting me. He's not going to stop. I have to keep fighting. I'm going to stop fighting.*

I made every effort to get out from under him. I thought he was killing me.

I thought that maybe if I stopped fighting him, he would stop hurting me.

"Get off me. Get off!"

He was so heavy. I felt suffocated. I couldn't bear his weight on top of me. I couldn't scream or fight any longer.

"Stop. Stop. Alex. Please stop. You're hurting me. Stop—please."

I couldn't believe he wouldn't stop.

I felt an unusual sensation between my legs. Pressure. Pushing. More pressure. He continued to thrust his penis inside of me. I screamed as loud as I could. And then I screamed some more.

"Stop it! Stop it! You're hurting me! You're hurting me!"

He just kept thrusting and pushing. It was like I wasn't even there. He was over me, slamming his huge penis into me again and again. I was screaming over and over or him to stop. I saw him shake his head and look down at me, as if he had just remembered me. I thought for sure he would stop then, and explain, somehow, what had just happened. But he didn't. He pulled back, slammed into me again. I felt like I would split open, like burned skin, like overripe fruit. I screamed again.

"Be quiet," he ordered. He put his hand over my mouth.

I was pinned to the bed. I couldn't move. I couldn't breathe. I felt flattened by his weight, by his hand covering the lower half of my face, while at the same time I felt pierced, impaled, invaded by his hard, sharp thrusts. There was something about trying to accept these two feelings at once that made me fear I was going to lose my mind. I gave up trying to scream. I lay motionless, enduring the pain. It was worse, and worse, and worse.

Oh, God, I'm going to die. I can't bear it.

Finally he stopped as abruptly as he had started and I felt such a relief because I was still alive. I thought what Alex had just done to me was going to kill me. I sat up slowly and right there, on the sheets near my knees and my ankles, were jagged-edged large blots of bright new red blood. I got that I was no longer a virgin. Oh my God.

"*Oh my god! Ohmygodddd!*" I was pointing to the blood and screaming. "*What did you do? WHAT DID YOU DO?*" I was furious. I felt close to hysteria. I started to scream.

"See what you've done. You've hurt me. Look what you did!" I pointed to the blood spots. "Take me home. I never want to see you again!" I was naked, my body folded protectively, clutching my knees to my chest and rolling convulsively across the bed as Alex moved around the room, wanting to keep distance between us. I was sobbing, gulping air, tottering between complete screaming hysterical rage and the gut-wrenching tears I could feel pressing for release at the back of my eyes. At that moment, we heard Alex's family coming in the front door. We both panicked.

"It's your parents!" I nearly started screaming again. Alex was running around the room, scooping clothes off the floor with one hand. He grabbed my wrist hard and started to pull me off the bed.

"It must be close to dinnertime," he said, his voice low and desperate. "We've got to get out of here." We heard their voices. Alex looked at the sheets. I was in shock. I slid across the bed as he pulled at me, nearly causing me to fall off the edge. He shoved the bundle of my clothes into my arms, pushed me towards the bedroom door, and started to tug the sheets off the bed.

"Get dressed in my room," he ordered. "I'll take care of the sheets." I stood there, frozen, naked and trembling, staring at him through glazed eyes. Did he think I cared about the sheets? He said it as if we were partners in this crime, as if we were dividing up the responsibilities of the cover-up.

I was in shock, odd and disconnected thoughts careening through my muddled mind. Even as I stood there in Alex's parents' bedroom, watching my boyfriend who had just raped me strip the sheets off the bed, I thought about the fact that we had not really seen each other naked in daylight before, and I remember thinking about how I must have looked and how he looked. He did have a lot of dark hair all over his body, especially around his penis. Alex interrupted my thoughts.

"Get your clothes on!" he snapped, his arms full of sheets stained with my blood. I fumbled with my panties, swaying drunkenly as I tried to pull them on. I couldn't seem to remember how to dress myself. I could barely put on my underpants and tried to put on my bra.

Alex pointed and whispered and motioned where I should go. He led the way taking my clothes, just in time. His parents were coming down the hall, past the sunken living room and toward the two bedrooms at the back of the apartment. I crossed the hall and ran into the bedroom Alex shared with his sister, still only half dressed. I pulled up my shorts and struggled with the buttons. I remember my heart pounding. I heard Alex tell his sister that I was in the bedroom and she shouldn't go in.

"It's okay," I heard her shout to me in a friendly voice, a reassuringly normal voice. "I'm in the bathroom. Take your time."

When I came out of the bedroom, dressed, hair combed and cleaned up as much as possible, I tried to act as if nothing had happened. I said a quick hello to his sister and I thought how attractive and nice she seemed. She was only a year or two younger, but I felt so old now. I felt so envious of this girl. I was hurting. Alex was waiting for me in the dining room.

"Take me home," I said in a low voice, "right now." I tried to say a nice hello and smile to his mother. His father was seated in the living room reading the newspaper. We walked out of the front door of his house. I was humiliated and in shock.

On the way home, I yelled and screamed at Alex, accusing him of violating my wishes. I couldn't tell myself that this was a rape. I just couldn't handle the thought of being raped by my boyfriend who I thought I loved. Back then, I blamed myself. It was poor judgment. It was my failure. It was Alex's victory. It was locker room talk and the stuff of his fantasies.

Alex drove without speaking, and at the curb in front of my building, I sprang from the car without a word. I thought of how this had happened. We never discussed doing anything more than what we had always done. Alex knew what I wanted and how I felt. How could this have happened? I could never have imagined anything at all like what I had just experienced.

There wasn't anyone I could tell. When I got home, I went over and over what had happened. I was dying to talk to someone, but I didn't know who. I spent the night silent: anxious, angry and upset. My body hurt all over, but my heart hurt worse. He broke my heart. I had no idea how to process this. Somehow, if it had been a stranger—that bad man hidden in the dark shadows about whom my mother always warned me—I think I could have found some way to understand it. But how can we ever understand evil in the people we've loved, the people we would have sworn before any God were good and would never hurt us?

What are the consequences of being hurt so deeply by someone we've loved and trusted? For me at nineteen, the consequences were so confusing I am still trying to understand them. When Alex raped me, I lost the possibility of a future with him; I lost him as a friend, companion, partner, boyfriend. I lost *us*; the idea of us a couple. But even before the rape that was an idea I had resisted, at least on the surface. It took losing Alex to this violent act to make me realize I had loved him. Even now, all these years later, the tangle of emotions and bad acts that marks that period of my life can make me dizzy. Alex loved me but I couldn't love him back because he wasn't the "right" kind of boy. I felt desire when I was with Alex, lust and a hunger for touch, which I couldn't indulge because I needed to be a "nice" girl. I knew I shouldn't love Alex, but just as my feelings for him were deepening and becoming more real to me, before I ever had the chance to come to terms with that, to rise to the occasion, to follow my heart instead of the rigid conventions of my upbringing, before I ever had the chance to love Alex back, fully and openly, he raped me.

In 1959 there was no term for what Alex did to me; an awareness of "date rape" was still decades away and it would be years before I knew to call it that. Mostly I tried not to think about it, but when I did, I would get angry all over again at the fact that Alex "took my cherry." That was the language I used; that was the way it was described back then. A girl's "cherry," her virginity, was constantly threatened and her job was to protect it at all costs. I had failed at my primary task, and Alex had won the contest. Always before Alex would stop when I insisted. Why on this night had he not stopped? If my rapist had been a stranger, I could have constructed the attack in a way that made sense. But he wasn't a stranger, he was Alex—Alex who had held me in his arms and danced with me, sang to me, drove hundreds of miles to see me, gave me a gold locket and told me he loved me. I have tried hard to understand how this event came to pass, and I know that just as I was and am a product of my time and place, so was and is Alex.

In 1959, when he raped me, he was a boy raised to accept his predator identity in the same way I was raised to accept my chaste one. And he was an athlete, and a deeply sexual person. But unlike me, he struggled not to suppress his sexuality, but to satisfy it. An opportunity was created by Alex, an opportunity to satisfy his urges, and he seized it. In a way, it was like basketball, Alex's other passion. When a basketball player sees an opening, he goes for it. I was the basket, the receptacle; the convenient hole, the place to get off.

That night, as I tossed in bed, the gold locket Alex had given me swung between my breasts, and it irritated me. I felt like it represented dishonesty of the highest order. There was no way to reconcile the two boys I knew: the one who had given me this locket, and the one who had, just hours before, held a hand over my mouth as he forced his penis into me. I didn't know which one to believe in, but I did know the truth of the pain between my legs, the blood on the sheets, my lost virginity. By the time the sun rose, ending that sleepless night, I had decided I hated Alex. I never wanted anything to do with him again, and I was suddenly desperate to tell him off.

But it was still too early, barely sunrise, and, good girl that I was, I knew I had to wait until an acceptable hour to call. I was wide awake, pacing, muttering to myself. Rage was coursing through my body. I felt feverish and explosive. What could I do? How could I hurt him back? The only thing I could think of to express my anger was to rip the locket off my neck. I wanted it to disappear, along with all the feelings I associated with it: love and trust and security. How could I ever have believed in Alex as a source of those things?

I threw the locket into the toilet and flushed it. The gold pendant and chain disappeared. I felt relieved, dismayed, happy, very, very angry and very, very sad. My stomach was in knots.

"Good. Good. Good," I thought to myself. What next? Finally I got back into bed, waiting for a decent hour to call Alex's house and tell him what I did and how I felt. It seemed a pathetic revenge next to what he had done to me, but it was all I had.

At eight a.m., I dialed his home telephone number. His mother answered.

"Good morning Mrs. Kinsler," I said. My voice sounded strange to me, although Alex's mother seemed perfectly normal. "Can I please speak to Alex?"

Alex got on the phone. He had barely said hello before I started speaking, slowly, in an angry voice, emphasizing each word individually: "I want you to know that I flushed the gold locket and chain you gave me down the toilet. I hate you. I never want to see you again."

I hung up. I broke down. I cried. I couldn't tell anyone.

It wasn't until over a year later, when I returned from my junior year at the University of Barcelona in 1960 that I saw Alex again.

I remember that summer, after the rape, I looked forward to my departure with desperate anticipation. I just wanted to get away: from Alex, from Brooklyn, from my abandoned father who was drinking too much, and from my demanding sister. I told no one what had happened to me, but I never stopped being furious. It burned inside me. Alex and I did not speak for the remainder of that summer; we did not try to "work through" this trouble in our relationship. There was nothing to work through. He hurt me.

He kept on hurting me. He heard me begging him to stop, and he didn't stop.

I was consumed by rage to the point that I knew if I didn't find a way to block out what had happened to me, I would never be able to move on with my life. So I worked on making Alex disappear. But to do that would mean losing all the wonderful memories I had of my time with Alex; the happiest time of my life; the only time I had ever felt secure and loved and acknowledged. I couldn't stop myself from comparing every man I met to Alex; the Alex who sang with me while his little car sped down the highway and the wind whipped my hair… not the Alex who raped me.

I dated a few men—Spanish and American—while I was in Barcelona, and I tried to stay busy and far away from memories of Alex. But once again my body betrayed what I thought were my best intentions and I found myself, while in Spain, consumed by ferocious feelings of sexual desire. Images of Alex and memories of his touch would wash over me at unexpected moments, and I would imagine making love with him—tender, passionate, consensual, I would imagine how his penis might feel inside me, as if it never had been. What I realize now is that I had succeeded in making the rape disappear by replacing it with a compassionate version of sex, a version in which I was a willing participant, and in which I was left satisfied and feeling cherished, rather than abused and feeling discarded. I re-made Alex in my mind, and clung to that man, to the exclusion of all others.

When I came back to New York, my father and sister were settled in Queens, and I moved into the new apartment. One night Alex came to take me out. We drove to Manhattan to visit his rich uncle who lived on Park Avenue. I guess he was trying to impress me, or make up with me. Or maybe this was his idea of an apology. Both his uncle and his aunt were warm, nice, and down-to-earth, like Alex's parents. I liked them a lot. We had drinks and food. I was supposed to be impressed, but seeing Alex again had unleashed all those feelings of rage I thought I had conquered. I tried to be charming and act high class, as my mother had trained me to do. I was definitely confused about my feelings for Alex. I had come to my own conclusion that I must keep my distance because I definitely did not want to be married to someone who was a gambler and not able to pay the rent. Somehow I forgot that I also did not want to be married to someone who would attack me, rape me, hurt me and not listen to me. I fixated on the issue of security and denied the rape to myself. I said a cold goodbye to him that night.

CHAPTER NINE

After Mitchell's birth, I was in a postpartum depression. The doctor confirmed it. I knew it before the doctor told me. I had gained more than fifteen pounds. My hormones were out of balance. My new life was daunting. It was different than anything I had expected. I now had a precious baby boy. But I didn't feel as if I had anything else. My expectations of married life and motherhood were more than disappointing. Empathy did not flow either way between Eli and me. Since sex wasn't allowed for at least six weeks after delivery and on top of that, Eli and I were sexually incompatible, our sex life was nonexistent.

My father, whom I loved so much, was in the hospital recovering slowly from what was then very experimental open-heart surgery. My husband was rarely around, my baby was colicky, and when I looked at my life I saw zero potential for a happy future. When Lila Kinsler told me that Alex wasn't married and lived in my neighborhood, I thought of him as an old friend. I had buried the experience of being raped so deeply it was almost easy to deny it. And when I did think about it, I remembered it as my sin, my fault, for not being more diligent in protecting myself. But mostly, if I thought of the rape at all, it was something that just was. I wanted to forget about it because there was so little love in my life, and my memories of Alex, before the rape, were rich and full of happiness.

Alex and I talked on the phone like what I wanted to believe we were—old friends catching up. I told him where I was living, right near him, that I was married and I had a three-month-old son. He invited me over to have dinner. Eli wasn't going to be home and my housekeeper, Mary, stayed with Mitchell. I walked over to Alex's house. It was right there on East Fiftieth Street, between First and Second Avenues. The building was a typical Manhattan high rise with a doorman and a furnished lobby. I announced myself and the doorman rang me up. I rang Alex's bell. He opened the door and as I walked in, he put his arms around me and I put my arms around him. It felt so good to be with my old friend again. We sat down at the dinette set, catching up. I found out that he was working at an engineering firm and his job was okay. I told him about finishing my Master's, and about my baby. Alex listened and asked questions and fidgeted. I thought he hadn't changed much at all.

Finally he asked me about Eli. I was eager to tell him about my marriage. There was no one else I could tell.

"My husband and I don't have a good relationship," I said. "I'm not attracted to him." Alex was quiet, and I felt a little embarrassed. Maybe I had gotten too personal. Then he looked up at me and grinned.

"I'm starving," he said. "How about we order out Chinese food?" I laughed. I was thinking about pistachio ice cream and how he always ate off my plate, and I felt comfortable. The years seemed to melt away. I hadn't felt this lighthearted in a long time.

"Sure," I said.

While we waited for the food, I think we may have danced a little. All that I can remember is that it felt wonderful to see his big, funny, happy smiling face, his in-shape body, to hear his nice-sounding voice and look into his warm hazel eyes.

After the food had arrived and we finished it all, including those hard noodles in the crinkly wax paper bag and there wasn't anything more to eat, we passed through the living room and wound up in his bedroom, which was furnished with a small bed and dresser and had a single window.

I knew I was in dangerous territory. I had told him on the phone, when we made our plans for dinner, that nothing could or would ever happen again. I told him when he led me to the bedroom that all I wanted to do was to talk. I just wanted to talk.

As I stepped into his bedroom I immediately remembered and brought up the rape in his parents' bedroom so many, many years ago. He sat down on the bed. And, as I also sat down on the bed, I said, "This is as far as it goes." I thought back about all the blood on the bed sheets of his parents' bed. While we were talking, I tried to get some information from him.

Who were you engaged to?

What happened?

Who broke the engagement?

Why?

Did you love her?

Did she love you?

How long after you broke up did you meet your present fiancée?

I wanted to know all about his life. I wanted to know what kind of woman he turned to after me. I wanted to know what kind of woman would leave him. Then I asked him about his current fiancée.

"Are you in love with her?" I asked. He didn't answer, and then he did but it was a noncommittal answer, maybe a shrug or a nod or something. I know it wasn't a straight yes or no. I was a little jealous, and I tried to get more information. He shrugged off all my questions.

"Oh—I don't know," he finally said in response to my persistence.

All of a sudden, using all of his weight, Alex pinned me down on the bed. I mustered all of my strength and tried to get him off of me. I tried to wriggle out from under him. But no use. He was ripping off all of my clothes. Everything.

As he mounted himself on top of me, I tried to wriggle out from under him and screamed, "Don't come inside me," and then repeated it. "Alex, I don't want you to come inside me." Part of me knew I shouldn't have been there, shouldn't have been on his bed with him in the first place, shouldn't have gone over to his apartment alone. *Don't come inside me.* So that when he did, I felt such a surge of rage and anger that he disregarded my request. He said he wouldn't and then he did, and it was so much like the first rape in his parents' bedroom. I had been raped again, by the same man. I had been completely violated. Again.

After a few minutes, I sat up and the anxiety immediately overwhelmed me. *Oh, my God*, I thought. *What if I get pregnant?* I hadn't had sex with Eli since before Mitchell's birth. *What am I going to do?*

I was upset, and I turned to Alex. "What if get pregnant?" I said, near tears. "Why did you do that? I said that I just wanted to talk, and you forced me against my will. You even came inside me!" I was frantically gathering my clothes. I needed to get out of there before my rage and terror shut

me down completely. Alex just watched me from the bed—
not speaking, or comforting, or apologizing. I was furious.

"I never want to talk to you again," I spat at him as I was
leaving. I hissed angrily at him, "I never want to talk to you
again." And except for once, I haven't.

On the walk home, I agonized over what to do. I just felt
sure in my gut that I was pregnant. Of course, I didn't have
any evidence. It was my intuition talking. It was Jewish guilt.

Jewish guilt is very specific. I suppose it is loosely
connected to some tenet of Jewish law, some ancient prin-
ciple of balance: bad acts are punished by a God whose job
is to exact retribution from His subjects, so that they will
refrain from sinning again. I'm not sure anybody can clearly
articulate this particular subset of guilt, but every Jewish
person is familiar with it. It is based on an exaggerated
sense of what the right thing is, which means we hardly
ever achieve it, which means we always feel guilty and we
always expect punishment. And since the punishment is
exacted by God, there is no point in trying to evade it. For
this reason, Jewish people are prone to confession. It just
seems more efficient.

I felt guilty. I felt so guilty. No question about it.
Although I had been raped, I didn't have sex with any man
other than my husband, and now God was going to punish
me. And that punishment, I had decided as I walked home
that fateful evening, was pregnancy.

I decided that if I were pregnant, I would just have the
baby and let Eli be the father. After all, I was married and
I already had a son, so there wasn't anything wrong with
having a second child. In the blocks between Alex's apartment and mine, I made a plan.

When Eli got home, I had to act as if I wanted to have sex
with him. I was operating on pure adrenaline and desperation, and for the first time since my disastrous advance

during our honeymoon, I initiated sex. We had dinner and then we went into the bedroom. Even though I didn't feel like it, I coaxed Eli into having sex. There wasn't much foreplay and for the first time in my life, I faked having an orgasm. After Eli came, I doubled my knees forward as I lay on my back. I acted out the part I felt was necessary. I had read that this awkward posture increased the chance of fertilization after sex, and if I was pregnant, I wanted Eli to remember this night. I must have stayed that way for fifteen minutes, as Eli walked in and out of the room. Every time he came near the bed, I would say something about pregnancy. *I just know I'm pregnant! I can just feel it. I think we just made a baby! Just watch and see.*

It makes me wince to admit this now. I can see her, that desperate girl with her legs in the air, pretending to her husband while she nurtures a dark, poisonous secret. I can see her, remember being her, and feel at once both sympathy for her and shame.

I missed my next period, and the test proved that I was pregnant. There didn't seem to be any choice but to just go through with it. I knew that it must be Alex who was the father, but I was married to Eli. I thought about the situation for a couple of days and held off telling Eli. I had saved Alex's office telephone number where he was working as an engineer. I went downstairs to the street to a public telephone. I put in the coin. I dialed the number. I was hoping for Alex to rescue me. I was hoping for him to suggest that we take my son and go away, get married and have our baby together. If he had crooked his finger, I would have grabbed Mitchell and run to him. I felt poised on the edge of a precipice. Alex might pull me back up, pull me into his arms. Or, with the tiniest flicker of a push; with a puff of a breath less than he would need to extinguish a candle, he could send me toppling over the edge.

"Alex, I'm pregnant," I said when he came on the line.

"Why are you telling me?"

"Because it's yours. From the night you raped me." I lowered my voice to a whisper and held the phone so tight against my mouth that it hurt me. "You came inside me," I tried to explain.

"Yes," was all he said.

"So, Alex, I'm pregnant," I continued, near tears, wanting him to say something. "What should I do?"

"I don't know," he replied flatly.

I hung up the phone and began my slow-motion tumble into the abyss.

That was the last time I ever spoke to Alex. That was in 1967. That was thirty-nine years ago.

CHAPTER TEN

Mitchell was barely three months old when I was pregnant again. Even under the best of circumstances—a happy marriage and a healthy mind—I wouldn't have wanted to be pregnant again so soon. Carrying a baby is hard on your body. I was still smoking, and I knew I should quit before I thought of having another baby. Mitchell was a high-maintenance infant and I wanted to devote myself to him, to comforting him through the colic, and to enjoying his happy times. But I was pregnant again and I was carrying a secret. The baby's father was not my husband.

I was in psychic shock. I wanted to turn back the clock. I wanted a do over. But at twenty-seven years old, the list of things I wished I could do over was already long, and I was finally starting to realize that there were no do-overs. You didn't get to go back and fix your mistakes. You had to live with them: the man on the other side of the bed you should never have married; the one you should never have loved because he was going to break your heart twice; the flutter in your belly you should never have made. I felt like my life was over; the weight of all these mistakes was just dragging me under and I didn't have the strength to resist.

I thought about an abortion. In 1967, we were still five years from legalizing it, but I had an idea there were ways to obtain one. One afternoon, a few days after my positive pregnancy test, I went to visit my friend Madeleine, who lived two floors below me in the same building. She was the kind of woman who knew things; she was something of a gossip and had always seemed very worldly to me. Over tea at her dining room table, I talked about Mitchell—what a sweet baby he was, but how I was finding new motherhood to be so much more exhausting than I'd expected.

"God, if I were to have another one right now. . . ." I said with forced casualness. "I don't know what I'd do." Madeleine didn't rise to the bait, so I continued nervously. "What *do* women do?" I asked.

Madeleine gave me a searching look. "There are ways," she said. "Places. It's legal in Puerto Rico. Doctors here know doctors there. You have to find the right doctor."

"Is it expensive?" I asked, looking down at my cup. Madeleine said she didn't know for sure, but she'd heard a Puerto Rican abortion could cost over $1,000, plus the airfare and hotel. "But you can go there and back in one day," she added, and I shuddered.

I thought about it. How could I possibly arrange it? No way. I felt far too humiliated to ask my gynecologist, and I knew Eli didn't have the money. I didn't and I certainly wasn't going to ask my father. What to do? I didn't want to have this baby, but I didn't want an abortion, either. I knew in my heart that even if I had the money and a sympathetic doctor, I still couldn't do it. I just didn't believe in killing anything; especially a baby. So I prepared myself to tell Eli we were expecting another baby.

My husband seemed neither particularly pleased, nor especially dismayed to hear that we were expecting another child so soon after Mitchell. His master plan had always included two children, and since he would be neither carrying nor caring for this baby, timing really wasn't important to him. He accepted the news with his typical distraction, and since we had just prepared for a baby less than two years ago, there really wasn't much to do. I had my doctors, although I found a new obstetrician. We had Mitchell's clothes and toys and furniture. We told our families, who accepted the news with little fanfare. It is first babies, or first boys, that excite Jewish families. And since our first baby was a boy—the *boychick!*—who can do no wrong, who is destined for greatness, who becomes the focus of his widely extended family—the fact of my pregnancy was received with irritating nonchalance. Had this been a planned baby about which I was excited, I would have been deeply hurt by the lack of enthusiasm, which seemed so unfair to me. But I was scared and ashamed and depressed over this pregnancy, and the neglect of both families was a relief to me. It was hard enough to get through every day. If I had had to pretend in front of in-laws, or my father and sister, I think I would have broken down completely. As it was, I barely kept it together.

I knew I couldn't tell anyone, and I was terrified that I might slip up and reveal the truth. Then Eli would find out and I could only imagine the worst things when I thought of that possibility. So I couldn't go out and be with people. My pregnancy was going okay, except for the smoking, but the secret weighed on me like a tumor, and the guilt grew steadily. I kept trying to hide from myself and I slowly started to withdraw from friends and family. I became a recluse. Sometimes I would remember how I felt during my first pregnancy: healthy, pretty, animated with optimism. I would remember how I read everything I could find about childbirth and infants, how I would talk on the phone all the time to my friends and our families; I would remember how proud I was of my blossoming stomach and how much I enjoyed putting on pretty, feminine maternity clothes and going out during the day. Now I never went out, never called anyone, barely cared about my appearance. I did my best to take care of myself, but I was slipping into a mire of depression and I couldn't pull myself out.

Eli seemed oblivious to everything. I was getting bigger and bigger. I was getting angrier and angrier. As the weeks passed and I followed up with my doctor visits, I resented being pregnant. I hadn't even gotten over the extra pounds I had gained from the first pregnancy and I was already pregnant again. I tried to calm myself. I tried to think of the baby growing steadily inside me. I knew I was carrying another boy, and I tried to send him good energy. I didn't want to poison him with my depression. None of this was his fault.

At the same time, Mitchell was growing in leaps and bounds. I was so pleased with all his new tricks. There was crawling first and then the first pair of shoes. There was baby talk like "blankey," and there was "Mama!" when he wanted attention. Major growth and new strides were happening every day for baby Mitchell, and I fought my depression and anxiety so that I could be present in his life. Sometimes he expressed interest in my growing belly, but I never talked to him about his brother, and that made me sad. I would imagine a different life for Mitchell and me: a family that could welcome a new baby with a clear conscience, joy and unsullied love. But we didn't have that. I had only a big guilty secret to match my big belly.

As the weeks passed, I would lie awake at night worrying about the baby: would he be healthy? What if he looked like Alex? What if Eli found out that the baby I was carrying wasn't his? But every time I asked that final question of myself, the same thought came to me: *I should tell him. I should tell Eli the truth. I have to tell him. But I can't.*

By the third or fourth month, I could feel the life inside me; the baby kicked and turned, and I was so glad. I was afraid my terror and guilt could harm him. I was completely withdrawn, nervous and more frightened than I had ever been in my life. I wasn't sleeping at night. I would lie next to Eli, tossing and turning as thoughts whirled through my brain. Should I or shouldn't I? In the beginning of my pregnancy, I had thought I could pull it off; I had thought it didn't really matter who the father was; either way I was his mother. That would never be in question. But the more these thoughts darkened my conscience, the more I came to realize that there was only one answer because there was only one truth. This lie I was carrying was growing in weight and toxicity until I couldn't take it anymore. I needed to tell Eli. He had the right to know, and I knew that concealing that truth was wrong. I think I would have rather been dead than have to face all of this, but I wasn't suicidal. I just couldn't live with the lie. My growing belly mocked me and I just couldn't live with it.

Weeks passed. I spent lots of days alone at home. I was getting sadder and sadder. I needed to talk about the situation. I should be able to talk to my husband. What would Eli do to me? He might even try to hurt me. Well, I would have to chance that because I just couldn't go on the way I was. I was literally bursting to tell Eli the truth. But I waited for the right moment.

One night, when I was in my seventh month, Eli came home early enough to have dinner with Mitchell and me. I didn't know for sure that I was going to tell him that night, but for weeks I had been wired, coiled like a spring, waiting. The truth weighed so heavily on my heart and on my body. I felt like I was carrying stones and all I wanted was to shed them before they crushed both my baby and me. After dinner, I was in the nursery with Mitchell when I heard my husband enter our bedroom. I laid Mitchell in his crib and followed Eli, shutting the door gently behind me.

He was standing by the window, and he turned to me. "I need to tell you something important," I said, the words sticking in my throat. I gulped air. I was so frightened. I laid my hands protectively over my bulging stomach and continued.

"I saw Alex," I said. His face clouded for a moment as he tried to remember who I was referring to. Then it dawned on him. The only time we had ever spoken about Alex was at our engagement party, when he asked me if I was a virgin. But I knew he remembered.

"About eight months ago," I continued, "I was invited for Chinese food at his apartment." It was so hard to get the words out. I had never rehearsed exactly how I would tell him, only that I needed to. "He lives in the neighborhood," I said weakly. Eli just stared at me. I took a deep breath.

"Do you remember the night I got pregnant?" My eyes dropped to my stomach for a moment, and then back to Eli. His face was hard and blank. I recalled lying on my back, my legs bent and elevated. I remembered how long I stayed in that position, my false enthusiasm, my desperate attempt to convince my husband he had just impregnated me. I knew Eli remembered it too. He still hadn't said a word. My hands were clenched at my sides as I went on.

"That was the night I—we had the Chinese food. Alex forced himself on me, against my will." Telling myself to look into Eli's eyes as I made this admission was torture, but I did it. And I saw crushed glass; glittery, feverish rage. A flush was creeping over his pale skin. But still he said nothing.

"Alex raped me!" The words, so long held inside me, tumbled out. "Afterwards, I came home and had sex with you. I wanted you to think you were the father."

Finally Eli spoke. His voice was low and murderous. "Are you sure it's Alex's child?" I nodded. I couldn't speak. I felt hysterical tears pushing at me, clogging my throat. As Eli turned away from me, the look of contempt and fury on his face turned me cold with terror: *Are you sure it's Alex's child?*

The fact that I *was* sure is testament to my cluelessness. Despite my education, my independent reading, my previous pregnancy and delivery, the ruthless way I would interrogate doctors for information; despite all that, I really knew nothing about the physiology of conception and pregnancy. I had the same vague ideas that most girls of that era had; there were no sex education classes or accessible reference books available to us, so we passed around half truths and wives' tales and sheer inaccuracies and thought we understood. I thought I understood how I had gotten pregnant; I understood about swimming sperm and fertile eggs. But I thought the father of my son had to have been Alex, because Alex muscled in there first. I thought conception happened instantly, and I believed I was already pregnant when I came home from Alex's apartment. I did entertain, for a moment, the possibility that it was Eli's sperm that had reached my egg. But that didn't seem feasible. Alex had a large penis and Eli didn't. I pictured fertilization like a race, and Alex's sperm had such a drastic head start. Of course, I thought, Alex was the father. Of course he was.

When I told Eli what I believed, it was with such certainty that he never questioned it, never challenged it, never dipped into his own limited knowledge of anatomy and physiology; he never considered the possibility that the baby I was carrying might be his. And for thirty-five years, neither did I. It would be that many years before I learned that fertilization is more like an obstacle course than a race, and that the "winning" sperm is not automatically the one that started first, but is more like the one clever enough to negotiate the route. It would be thirty-five years before I allowed myself even to consider the possibility that Eli and I, not Alex and I, could have made the baby we gave up for adoption. It would take an offhand comment from my son Moses during our first, three-hour phone call—*Where did I get these elephant ears from?*—to make me question, for the very first time, the paternity of the baby I carried that terrible year. Because Eli had had protruding ears. But until that moment, no one had challenged my version. *Are you sure it's Alex's child?* Eli asked me, and I said *Yes*.

"Yes." I stood frozen by the door to our bedroom. "I'm sure." Eli started pacing back and forth in front of the window, alternately putting a finger in his mouth or running his hands through his hair. He was thinking, plotting, looking for the loophole, I knew. I imagined him in a courtroom, his sharp mind working frantically to find the advantage, to turn around a losing case. I wanted him to say something. I felt like my knees would buckle from the fear and tension.

I suppose that in my naiveté I had hoped that Eli would appreciate the courage it took me to tell him the truth. It was a foolish and immature expectation, I know now, but at the time I thought that maybe, just maybe, Eli would decide to accept the baby. I thought that maybe we could raise this baby together, in honesty. It was the lie that was killing me, and my deepest hope was that Eli would forgive me in the interests of our family. I knew so little about men, about ownership, about humiliation and threatened manhood, and the lengths some men will go to avoid those things. But as I watched Eli pace in front of me like a penned and vicious animal, the deep furrows on his forehead getting

deeper as his thoughts played across his face in the form
of a grimace, I knew that I had expected a depth of understanding and forgiveness that he was completely incapable
of. I don't know that any man could have been. And it's not
as if we had a good marriage before this night.

I knew also that he was furious, more angry than I had
ever seen anyone, and my terror tripled. I thought he might
throw me out, put Mitchell and me out on the street with
no money, no place to go. Or worse yet, throw me out alone
without my baby.

I thought he might strike me. I thought he might kill
me. I thought he might throw me out the window. I reached
for the doorframe to steady myself. I needed him to say
something, but still he was silent.

"I'll do anything you want," I blurted out. "Please, don't
hurt me. Please." Tears were coursing down my cheeks.
"Please Eli, just tell me what you want me to do." He whirled
around and advanced across the room toward me and I was
sure he was going to hit me. I bent forward to protect my
stomach, and held up an arm, a feeble attempt to protect
myself.

"What do you want me to do?" I squeaked through my
terror. He was standing next to me now, his eyes flashing,
his breath coming in quick pants. And then he asked me
one more time: "Are you sure that it's Alex's?" His voice
was clipped and hard.

"Yes!" I sobbed. "Yes." I was leaning against the wall to
keep from falling, watching my husband through my tears.

"Then we have to get rid of it," he said, in the coldest
voice I had ever heard. I was crying and shaking my head.
"No, no abortion. I can't," I gasped for breath, "and it's too
late."

"You'll give it up for adoption," he said as he brushed past
me and reached for the door. "I'll find an adoption agency."

I was crying so hard I could barely speak, but I managed to reply. "Okay. Whatever you say." I don't think that what he was requiring of me really registered. I remember being so relieved that he wasn't going to kill me, or throw me out.

"And then you'll give me another child to make up for this." He was staring at me with hatred, and then he stepped forward and grasped my wrist. I flinched.

"Promise me we'll have another child *right away!*" I felt like the lowest, most worthless of human beings.

I promised.

⌇

The journey of the adoption agencies began. First we went to a Jewish adoption agency, but they would not take a Jewish baby for adoption, especially from the home of a married couple. They said we needed to work out our problems and keep the baby. Eli was firm and unmoved. I was numb. The adoption agency suggested that we go to a non-Jewish organization, called Special Care, where we were told that they would not take the baby for adoption unless I was willing to lie and say that one of the parents was Catholic. So I agreed.

I also agreed to and signed papers stating that I would give the baby away the night I gave birth. I agreed to give up all of my rights in the future. I signed all the papers. I couldn't even think about what they meant. I felt detached from everything around me. I felt as if every nut and bolt holding me together had been loosened to just before the point of release. I moved cautiously. I spoke in whispers. I never made eye contact. I felt like I was living in a dense fog, and I was glad. I didn't want to see clearly. I couldn't face what I had done, what I was about to do, what my life had become. Eli and I barely spoke.

My obstetrician suggested that it would be best to have my labor induced about three weeks before my due date; "You know, you don't have to go on with this all the way to the end," was how he put it. Dr. Tobias knew I was giving the baby up, so perhaps he thought he was being kind, although I felt judged. I felt like he and Eli were conspiring together to keep me hidden and to get rid of my baby as fast as possible. But I agreed to have my labor induced, and went all by myself to Dr. Tobias's office for a scheduled appointment. Under the circumstances, Eli didn't want to come. His need to punish me hadn't diminished from the night I told him about Alex, and he acknowledged my pregnancy only to instruct me about our plans and our cover story. The adoption papers were signed, and he told me we were going to tell people the baby had died during delivery, strangled on the umbilical cord. I nodded and made mental notes like a good student, and complied with the lie. I never argued or protested, and only once did I question the believability of Eli's story.

"What will we tell people about a funeral?" I asked Eli once.

"If the baby's born dead, it was never alive, so there's no need to have a funeral," he answered, in his lawyerlike "end of discussion" voice, and I complied. I believed I deserved this punishment. I believed I had to sacrifice my baby to atone for seeing my old friend, Alex. It was Jewish guilt once again rearing its ugly head. It was Jewish guilt that led me in the first place to confess and Jewish guilt which convinced me that Alex was the father of this baby. It would be years before the ugly truth became apparent to me; I didn't really know who the father was. It could have been Eli.

I went to the hospital. I got put out. I woke up in the recovery room without the big, big belly and without the baby.

I can remember rolling from side to side in the hospital bed, banging against the metal guards the nurses had pulled up on both sides. I rolled back and forth and forth and back. I thought about my Daddy. I thought about Mitchell squirming up and down his crib and banging on his metal guards. I thought of the baby and then forced those thoughts to go away. I felt like I was going crazy. I felt like such a "bad" girl. I wondered if guilt could kill you, because I couldn't imagine how I would live with this. How could I do such a thing? How could I give away a baby for adoption? What kind of a person was I? I was completely alone. My husband didn't visit, and as far as I know, he didn't call.

I couldn't stay still. A nurse came into my room and told me to settle down. "You need to be careful with the intravenous tube," she said, not unkindly. My left arm hurt like crazy. It was straight out on my left side, attached to a wooden board. I tried to move it but I couldn't. I was in a lot of pain. The reality of the situation was hitting me hard, right in the face, or rather right in my head. I never got headaches but now I had a very bad headache.

"Is the baby perfect?" I asked the nurse. She told me he was. "I want to see him,"

I said. My head felt like it would explode. I thought if I could just see him, it might help with the pain.

"You can't see him," the nurse answered, her voice tense. She wouldn't look at me. "You signed a paper saying that once you gave birth, you would give him away. You can't see him," she repeated, and left the room.

I started to cry and I kept yelling, "I want to see my baby! I want to see my baby! I want to see my baby!" until I fell asleep.

When I woke up I couldn't move. To this day, I'm not sure why; I don't know if I had been sedated, or restrained, or if I had some sort of hysterical paralysis. The room was

dark and I was alone and I couldn't move. I tried to accept
the fact that I had given away a baby, but I couldn't. I tried
to calm myself and say the words out loud: "You gave birth
to a baby, but it is not yours." But all that did was make
me sob so hard I couldn't breathe. I just wanted my baby.
I decided that if I screamed and yelled loud enough, they
would let me see him; maybe they would let me keep him.
I couldn't move, but I could scream.

"I want my baby. I WANT my baby! I WANT MY BABY!"
I was yelling and struggling in my hospital bed, and finally
I was able to sit up. I gulped in deep breaths and screamed
out my desperation as loud as I could, until finally a nurse
came in, a different nurse.

"Sshhh," she said gently. "I'll ask, okay. But you've gotta
calm down."

She came back in a few minutes. I was still crying hysterically, totally engulfed in emotion. She was carrying my
new baby son. She rolled up the back of the bed so I could
sit up straight. She released my arm from the board. Then
she handed me my baby. I reached for him as if he were
my lifeline.

"I want to be sure he's perfect," I whispered. So we
unwrapped him. I kissed him. My son. I couldn't believe
my eyes. I looked at and touched his tiny hands and feet
and counted them out loud although I could see them.

"I'll leave you two alone," the nurse said as she left the
room. "You can have fifteen minutes."

Those fifteen minutes would have to last thirty-six years.

The first thing I did was to kiss him several times. I held
him against my breasts, leaned over and inhaled him. He
smelled clean and pure. He smelled like flowers. He smelled
like love. He looked like he had a suntan. His skin was soft
and creamy and he had a full head of dark hair. He actually

looked just like my mother had described what I looked like when I was a newborn.

Then I talked to him: *I love you so very much. I know you will be better off where you're going. I know you will have a very charmed life. I know you will be a special person. I have no doubt about it.* His eyes were on my face. I knew he could hear me. He knew his mother's voice.

Remember that I will always love you. I will always be praying for you. God will always be watching over you. I kissed him again. This gorgeous little bundle was mine. No matter where he went from here, he was my baby. I wanted only the best for him. And that was not with Eli Kramer.

I lost my voice. I was whispering to the baby as the nurse returned to my room.

"It's time for feeding," she said. I let her take him from my arms. Oh, my God. Oh, my God!

Later that night, I was rolled into another room and given a sleeping pill. The next morning, after breakfast, I was told that my husband was there to take me home.

Eli came into my room. There wasn't any affection at all.

"Are you ready?" was all he said. I said I was.

"How's Mitchell?" I asked him.

"Fine."

Eli and I took the elevator down to the first floor. I remember walking out the big front door and down the steps into the sunlight. I could see trees. Eli carried the small suitcase. We got into a taxi, and somewhere in the building behind me was my son. I was leaving my son with strangers and it hurt so bad I had no choice but to push it out of my mind. I couldn't have lived otherwise. I couldn't have been a mother to Mitchell. I took a deep breath and followed Eli into the taxi.

"Sutton Place South," he told the driver. "Northeast corner of Fifty-seventh and Sutton Place." He settled himself on the vinyl seat, gave the driver our address and turned his face to the window, away from me.

⁂

It's like losing a limb. It's worse than losing a limb. It's living with a phantom. It's trying to love the son you still have while you struggle to forget the one you've left behind. It is psychic pain so deep and profound that all you can do is deny it. At least that's all I could do. I came back to my beautifully decorated apartment, my empty marriage, my delicious baby and forced myself to forget about the child I had given away. I was never really successful at that.

Eli was determined that I keep my promise and give him another baby, and he was very aggressive about trying. Suddenly we had a sex life, when we'd never had one before. And it was worse. It was terrible; it was degrading. All through our courtship and the early years of our marriage, Eli's lack of desire and the infrequency of our lovemaking had been a huge source of dismay for me. In fact, I remember a specific night before my first pregnancy, when we were watching TV. There was a talk show with a Manhattan based female therapist who had a practice in Greenwich Village. Her specialty was frigidity in women. I decided that night that since our sex life was nonexistent, it must be my fault. I must be frigid. The next day I called information, got the therapist's telephone number and made an appointment to see her. She told me that I would never be able to change the situation and that I should get a divorce. I didn't remember at the time, or else I blocked it out; this was almost exactly what my father had told me, six months into this marriage. I remember responding to the therapist that if I wanted a divorce, I would just go ahead and get it. I had come to talk to her because I wanted to work things out.

After I left her office, I called Eli on the phone. I told him exactly what the therapist said about getting a divorce.

"Do you want to split up?" he asked me matter-of-factly, and I said no. Before the birth and surrender of my second son, I genuinely wanted to make my marriage work. I wanted to keep my vows and give my children two loving parents in the home. I wanted intimacy, lovemaking, a friendship with my husband. But after I lost Moses, I lost my will to try. I lost my natural optimism and my ability to pretend. And not only did I cease to lament the lack of sex in my marriage, I welcomed it. Sex was the last thing I was interested in. It was so linked to love in my mind and in my heart, and love, loving—Alex, my lost baby, myself— had left me destroyed. I was terrified to love and sex was the last thing I wanted. But Eli insisted. I kept my promise.

It took a long time for me to get pregnant, but Eli wanted another child very badly. He kept track of my cycle and I came to dread the nights when I knew he would say *We're gonna do it tonight* or *We have to try tonight.* It was awful sex, mechanical and emotionless. I would lie beneath Eli feeling like a test tube, a hole, a garbage can, a baby-making machine. But I did it, whenever I was told to, without complaint. I had already lost Moses. Another baby wouldn't replace him, although Eli believed it would, and I had promised to give him that. I felt like I owed it to him. He was my husband. I made a promise.

After grief, the strongest emotion I felt was guilt.

After two years of trying, Eli finally got his wish. I was pregnant.

CHAPTER ELEVEN

Jared was born in New York City, in 1969. I didn't have any pregnancy problems, and the delivery went smoothly. I didn't need stitches this time, and I recovered quickly. I remember what a pleasure it was to hold Jared in my arms without the physical pain I felt when Mitchell was born. And I remember that it was so much better to come home with a baby than without one.

Every detail of my third pregnancy and delivery, every detail of Jared's infancy would lead me to a memory of the baby I gave away, and depression would overwhelm me. Trying to access those memories now has the same result, and I am reminded again and again of how deeply I failed my third son, who paid the price for circumstances over which he had no control. For the two years that I lived with Jared before his father moved out behind my back, taking the children with all their clothes and furniture, my marriage was deteriorating—how could it not?—and I was overwhelmed with sadness.

When I came home from the hospital with Jared, I told everyone that he was the best baby in the world. After experiencing a hyperactive baby like Mitchell, Jared seemed exactly the opposite. There was hardly a whimper. He hardly seemed to move. Any time I looked into the room to see how he was, he was complacently just being.

He liked to be held. He was sweet and smiled easily. He seemed like a very internal baby, interested in some inner world that didn't involve me. He didn't really talk or express specific likes or dislikes until he was almost one. He ate and drank his bottles. He loved his big brother. The most animated he ever became was when Mitchell came to play with him.

I thought there might be something wrong with him. I even took him to the baby doctor to ask about it. She told me he was fine, and that I should enjoy a peaceful baby after all the hours I spent herding and protecting and comforting my hyperactive and colicky first son.

Jared had fair skin, which was very sensitive. As a baby, he was prone to diaper rash, and as he grew, he suffered from food allergies that gave him terrible eruptions—angry red patches marring his pale skin. He had a long and ever-changing list of foods he couldn't eat, and often wore long sleeves and knee high athletic socks even in hot weather to cover up his red and raw skin, which looked like psoriasis. But he didn't complain. He is not a complainer. He was an easygoing baby who grew into an easygoing boy.

He was an accident-prone child. He'd had stitches twice before kindergarten—once over his eye when he was four and ran into a marble ledge in front of an apartment house, and another time when some exuberant play with blocks resulted in a deep gash. He had scraped knees and scratched hands, a spectacular black eye once when he was hit with a baseball bat, and more stitches when, in high school, a print shop mishap resulted in a nearly severed fingertip.

"Tell me about that," Jared said recently, after I made a casual reference to that print shop accident. "I had some accidents, didn't I?" I gazed at his face and nodded.

"You saw the inside of the ER much more than Mitchell," I answered. Jared looked distant, lost in memory. I could see him trying to re-create the event, put it in context, and I knew he had turned to me to help him do that. It was an oddly tender moment, a shared memory and the collaboration of recall: the closest thing to a mother/son connection my child would allow.

Jared has been very angry with me since he learned of the existence of Moses, his brother. He's hurt, and that hurts me. He has been distant, and on the few occasions I've seen him in the past three years, he seems determined to wound me, punish me. In that he has been largely successful. Moses would like to know his brothers better, and asked me if I would broach the subject with Jared. "I'd like to get together with him," Moses said. "Can you arrange it?"

I was terrified. It was all I could think of all afternoon. I was reasonably sure that Jared wasn't ready, but I felt obligated to extend Moses' offer.

With Moses' phone number written on a scrap of paper I had been clutching for the last hour, I approached Jared, trying to smile warmly and keep my voice casual. "I'd like to give you this," I said, holding out the square of paper. "It's Moses' number." His face was blank. "In case you ever want to talk to him."

We stood frozen for I don't know how long, my arm extended. Jared didn't reach for the paper, and as I searched his face, I saw it darkening. Prepare yourself, I thought. The storm is about to break.

And it did. Head shaking, foot stamping impatiently, snatches of an angry retort: *I don't believe you. . . . What am*

I supposed to do with it. . . . I didn't meet you so you could do this. . . . And then Jared said, in a cold voice:

"It took you thirty-five years to tell me I had another brother. I'll let you know when I'm ready, OK?"

I think he went on, but I didn't hear the rest.

From the time he was two, Jared lived with his father and I saw him every other weekend. I usually visited with the two boys together. Jared developed in a sort of emotionally detached way; detached from me, anyway. Jared looked up to Mitchell and in a way, Mitchell became Jared's caretaker. Until Jared married and had a son of his own, Mitchell was the most important person in the world to Jared.

Jared followed in Mitchell's footsteps and was sent to the Dalton School. This was not the right place for him. He was more creative than academic; more social than athletic. We made a mistake sending him to a school where he would forever be compared to his older brother, who had excelled there. Though he was terrific at softball and I can remember him playing the catcher's position at a game, he lost the desire to go to school and started to cut classes. He was better off at a private school where he could discover his passions: theatre, writing and acting. He was active in theatre groups both at school and at summer camp, and was performing Shakespearean protagonists by the time he was fifteen. Always a quiet, unassuming boy, it was amazing to see him expand and blossom onstage. When Jared acted, he *was* the character, released from his ever battling parents and the shadow of his overachieving brother; released from the embarrassment and burning itch of skin eruptions and the vigilance required by a restricted diet; by assuming another identity, my son could become himself.

We all thought it would be better for him to attend a city school. So in the last half of his senior year, he transferred to a special public high school in Manhattan where he got the chance to have internships and learn different trades. It was a good fit for this teenager who didn't want to sit still, who wanted to be doing. Even though he only attended for a year, he seemed to wake up and mature there. I could feel it and so could his father. On the day of his high school graduation, I wept with relief and pride. His father wept too. I had never seen Eli cry before and I never did again.

Jared has always been both independent and adaptable. He doesn't wait for permission to try something new, and when things don't work out, he moves on. He left New York for Los Angeles to pursue an acting career. And although he has received some financial help from his father and from Mitchell, he has mostly supported himself on his own terms. In L.A., he went to acting school and then decided to enroll in college.

Jared is married now, and has a little boy who is turning two this year. He lives in L.A. with his wife and son, and has a job producing shows at the Hollywood Bowl. He's turned out to be very good at it. He's an on and off vegetarian. He's had the same best friend since his childhood.

I don't think Jared has ever felt comfortable around me, and that doesn't surprise me. We had so little time together before his father stole him away, and the time we spent together afterwards was never very satisfying—we were both anxious and confused, I think, and for so much of his childhood I was struggling with every aspect of my life. My every-other-weekend visits with him and Mitchell were difficult for me, and I struggled unsuccessfully to maintain composure. I would break down in tears at both ends of the weekend—when they arrived, because the sight of my sons made me realize how much I had missed them, and when they left, because I had to part from them for two more weeks.

I've heard that humans don't remember much before the age of three. I don't know if that's true, and I don't know if I want it to be true. If it's true, it means that Jared has no memory of having his mother with him every day: bathing him, feeding him, pushing him on the baby swing; kissing him, singing to him, leaning into his crib to lay my hand against his cheek and feel his warm, sweet baby breath. It hurts me to think Jared remembers none of that. But at the same time, the first two years of his life were also the final years of my marriage to his father, and they were marked by pain and bitterness. If it's true that Jared has no memory of *those* years, then I would consider it a gift.

☙

Now I know that my marriage was over before it started. Now I know that there was no way for us to recover from the circumstances of the conception of my second son, and then from his surrender to strangers. Now I know that, even if there had been a way to heal Eli's fury, even if there had been a way to soothe my grief and despair over the adoption, even if we could have recovered from such severe trauma, there was nothing to return to. People marry for the wrong reasons every day. Now I know there is only one right reason to marry: love—heart-stopping, joyful, desire-filled, honest, gentle, compassionate love. Eli and I married for all the wrong reasons and then spent ten years hurting each other. My children were the victims of our bad choices.

Obviously, Eli and I had been drawn to each other by our differences; Eli's calm passivity meshing with my impatient energy. But people lose respect for differences and begin to defend themselves instead. Then we wound each other with the very things that once attracted us. Eli withdrew even farther from me, stopped speaking with me or even acknowledging me, and worked even longer hours. I became more frantic, more verbal, more needy. I met his resistant silences with a barrage of questions, demands and insults. Eli and I began and ended our marriage poles apart. There was no communication in any form. And of course, the most illusive, indefinable and unpredictable—but essential—element in marriage was missing. Love was missing.

I was home with two small boys, trying to care for them and be attentive to their needs. I was more experienced now as a mother, and much more relaxed with Jared. I didn't worry so much as I had with Mitchell. I knew how to do things for Jared and with him. And my sons were close. There was so much love between them. I never saw sibling rivalry. When four-year-old Mitchell would enter the room, baby Jared would light up and burble with joy. I loved the thought that they would be a unit for their lives. It made me wish that Sandra and I had managed to achieve that. But maybe sisters are different, I thought. All I knew was that I had this dream baby who never cried, who would lay contently where I put him, who loved his brother and loved me.

But I couldn't stop thinking about Moses. No matter how much I loved my boys, my third son wasn't there. It was like I could see the space in the room where he should be. I lived every day with this nagging feeling that I had forgotten something important, that something wasn't right. And then I would remember—I had left my son at the hospital. It was a pain that didn't disappear.

The summer after Jared was born, we rented a beach house for six weeks in Connecticut, in a gated community called Sandy Shores on the edge of the Long Island Sound.

I had been desperately looking forward to this sojourn out of the city: the apartment was oppressive to me, and Alex, as far as I knew, still lived a few blocks away. The boys could play outside, and Eli would only be coming up on the weekends. My husband and I were barely speaking to each other, and for the first time in our marriage, I was glad that he worked all the time; I was glad not to have to see him. Just the sight of my husband could cause me to dissolve into tears or explode with rage. Every time we spoke, I heard his voice again: *You'll give it up for adoption.* I knew I could never forgive him for the loss of my second son and for treating me like breeding stock. I felt irreparably damaged.

But really I couldn't forgive myself. *He* didn't surrender the baby. I did. I signed the papers. I handed my son over in the hospital. And I promised my husband another baby.

I didn't know how I would ever go on.

Eli's brother Barry and his wife Faye came up for a weekend. I had always liked them and I was looking forward to the company. The boys were happy to spend time with Uncle Barry and Aunt Faye, who were childless that weekend, having left their two sons with Faye's parents. Barry and Faye had always appeared to have a happy marriage, and I couldn't help comparing them to Eli and me. I found myself sinking deeper and deeper into desperation. Despite the clean natural setting and the good company, despite the fact that I loved Faye and Barry, being in that house with them was torturous. I would watch my in-laws all the time, from behind my book or sunglasses or across the dining room table while I pretended to fuss with Jared in his high chair. I would watch Barry play with my sons, and listen to Faye gush over them, seeing all their charms and talents and delights with a fresh eye. And I would watch this couple *together*—conversing about all kinds of things, laughing together, leaving for the beach hand in hand, working together in the kitchen—until I thought I would simply dissolve in my sadness; without meaning to, Barry and Faye made a mockery of the false life I was living in Manhattan with Eli.

Eli would arrive on Friday night from the city, and return Sunday evening. We barely exchanged a word when we were alone. I felt like a pariah; like an unworthy, unclean servant. I knew I was sinking into a mire of depression, but I didn't know how to save myself. I knew Eli was thinking of buying a house here, which is why he had wanted to rent this summer place. He thought it would be better for the boys. I was terrified this would happen; that he would move us up to this lovely but isolated place, where I would lose contact with the few friends I had left. I would lose the stimulation of the city. I feared being buried alive.

On this particular Saturday night, Eli was putting up a good front for his brother and sister-in-law: exchanging playful jokes and extending to me, if not warmth, at least courtesy. After we all said goodnight and went to our respective bedrooms, I couldn't fall asleep. With all of these feelings weighing down my spirit and making my mind race, I lay awake for hours next to Eli until finally, pulling the blanket off my bed, I wandered out of the house, barefoot and in my nightgown, and walked aimlessly toward the beach. I didn't know why I was going there. I thought maybe I would just keep walking, into the waves, past the waves, letting the water envelope me, cleanse me and eventually take me. I could see my boys—Mitchell and Jared—with Faye and Barry as their parents. I could see my nameless boy with the mother who did not leave him; he would never even know I was gone. If I just disappeared from that house, I thought, no one would miss me. If I disappeared, I would leave behind a perfectly balanced unit. I couldn't bear to see Eli on Fridays, when he came up from the city;

I couldn't bear the pretending. And I couldn't bear the void I saw every time I looked at my two sons, the void where their sturdy dark haired brother should be.

I got to the beach and stood at the shore, my blanket still bundled in my arms as I gazed out at the water. But I knew there was no escape for me there. I was tied to this life, as dismal as it felt right then. I loved my boys.

I stepped back from the tumbling waves, across the sandy beach, walking slowly until, for no particular reason, I chose a place to spread my blanket. I laid down and pulled the edges over me, but I couldn't relax. Even the sound of the waves didn't soothe me. I got up and paced across the beach, my mind racing. I returned to the blanket, laid down, and eventually slept, worn out from all the anguish.

The next morning I snuck into the house before breakfast. Nobody had noticed I was gone.

∽

Sometime in the fall after that summer, Eli and I started talking about divorce. Well, talking is something of an inaccuracy: screaming, sniping, cutting, insulting would probably be closer to the truth. Whatever animosity we had been holding in towards each other was released like poison gas. We couldn't have a civil conversation.

I hadn't worked since before my pregnancy with Mitchell, and was completely dependent on Eli for the necessary funds to run our household. Eli had always controlled our finances, even the money I came into the marriage with and my inheritance when my grandfather died in 1968. Any time I questioned him about something related to money, he would respond with "I'll take care of it," and for a time I believed he did just that. But I had long known that Eli was terrible at managing money, and had taken over writing the checks for basic household bills several years before, after I discovered quite by accident a drawer stuffed full of unpaid bills: credit accounts at local stores, utilities, some doctor bills; those things my husband had said he would "take care of." Still, I had no access to cash and one way Eli expressed his anger with me during this terrible time was to withhold the house money. He stopped leaving me the cash I needed to buy groceries and things for the boys, and for the first time in my life I had to scrounge. The irony of it is part of what kept me from seeking help from somebody, anybody; here I was married to an Ivy League educated lawyer, living in a luxury building in Manhattan's most exclusive neighborhood, and I was trying to feed my children for several days with a loaf of white bread and a dozen eggs. I had to shop farther and farther from my neighborhood because we owed money to so many of the local stores. The boys needed clothes, shoes and some kind of activity and I had money for none of it. I turned down invitations because I couldn't afford to see anybody or do anything. I was humiliated and helpless.

Eli came home after the boys were in bed every night, and slept on a mattress in the middle of the living room floor. Our animosity grew in leaps and bounds We both hired lawyers, but our resentment of each other was so great, and our finances so complicated, that there was no way we could reach a straightforward agreement. Eli had recently split from his law partner, and was practicing independently. His father had died two years after mine and left a tangled estate tied up in multiple business names and partners. And while I had no physical assets, I had nine years invested in this marriage and two small boys to raise. And I had given up a child. For him. For Eli. That's what I told myself as the battle raged between us. *I gave up a son for you.*

And I wanted something back. It was a recipe for disaster. It was two people who should have known better behaving badly. It hurt my sons.

One night Eli came home about one a.m., and I was watching TV in the living room. The television, which used to be in our bedroom, had been in the living room for weeks, since Eli moved it out along with one of the twin mattresses from our bed. Consequently, I rarely watched it any more. But I had spent a long day alone with the boys, most of it in the park. They had both been fussy about going to sleep, I had the kitchen to clean up, and when I finally had a chance to sit, I wanted to watch television.

So often these things start with something insignificant; so often we use something that doesn't matter to express our hurt. Because it's easier that way, I guess. All I know is that when I heard my husband's key in the door I knew he was going to tell me to vacate the living room—we had divided territory, and he had staked his claim to that part of the apartment—and I knew I was going to refuse. I had been living for months now in a war zone. Eli was trying to make me leave, but I had no place to go. I had two children under the age of six. I couldn't take much more, but I had no idea what to do. Half the time my lawyer wouldn't take my calls. I was too ashamed to turn to my father, too prideful to ask my mother for help, and too distant from my sister to find support there. Under such desperate circumstances, one would think that control of the television would be of less than minor importance.

"I'm going to sleep," Eli said as he took off his suit jacket in the foyer. "Leave."

"No," I answered, my eyes on the television. I couldn't have told you what I was watching. "I'm waiting for the news."

"It's one o'clock in the morning. The news isn't on."

"Yes, it is."

"Get out," he said, and I could hear the fury in his voice. I kept my eyes on the television and pretended to ignore him. And then I yelped in pain as one of Mitchell's wooden sculptures, something he had made in nursery school, hit me hard on the right foot. It shattered, and I looked from it to Eli, uncomprehending.

"Mitchell made that," I said softly. Then louder. "Your son made that!" I could see the back of Eli's dress shirt as he stormed into my bedroom—my territory. I jumped to my feet, gasping as my right foot throbbed, and hobbled into the room after him.

"What are you doing?" I screamed. He was in my closet, pulling out my clothes, tearing things off hangers and piling dresses, pants and blouses on the floor.

"Helping you pack, you whore." He crossed to my dresser and grabbed a stack of unopened mail. I hadn't had the heart, even, for that. "Whore," he repeated as he tore each letter in half. "Whore!" He ran to the bedside phone, picked it up and tossed it at me. "Call a friend," he said.

I felt anger flow through my body and grabbed the phone. "I'll call the police," I said. "You can watch TV from the cell where you belong, you arrogant bastard." I was dialing 911 as he flew across the room, grabbed the phone from me, threw it back onto the bed and wrapped his big, thick-fingered hands around my neck.

"Have me arrested," he growled, "and I'll be out in an hour. But you'll never see your kids again." He was choking me, and I was twisting and gasping, until I broke free and ran for the door. I couldn't wait for the elevator. I flew down the stairs and rang Madeleine's bell. It was nearly two AM, but she let me in, calmed me and looked at my neck.

"Call the police," she said, and handed me the phone.

What happened next is a blur, too painful to try and clarify. I know that I went back upstairs with Madeleine to wait for the police. I know that Eli was beyond furious—screaming at me, screaming at Madeleine, screaming at the police when they arrived. I know that there was a lot of negotiating and that the police discouraged me from pressing charges, but I did anyway. And I know that somewhere in all this chaos, Eli decided that Mitchell should "see everything" that was happening, and that he barged into the room where the boys were sleeping and came out pulling my sleepy eyed boy roughly by one arm.

"Your mother wants me to go to jail," Eli was saying to Mitchell. "Look," he pointed to the officers, "your mommy called the police."

That terrible night remains mostly a hazy memory. I don't want to relive it with too much detail. But one part of it is crystal clear: Mitchell, not yet six, in little boy pajamas, his brown hair tousled but his eyes wide and liquid, looking from his mommy to his daddy to the police officers with an expression of confusion and fear.

That is an image I will never forget.

Madeleine stayed with the boys while I rode in a squad car to the station and pressed charges against Eli for assault. Mitchell was up when I got home at seven a.m. Madeleine said he hadn't ever gone back to sleep.

For a while after that night, things were calmer, if not more reasonable, in our home. We tried at least to be civil in front of the boys. We avoided each other determinedly; I would be in my bedroom with the door closed long before Eli came home at night. There was no more television watching for me. Eli still played games with the house money, but I was exhausted from all the fighting and could do nothing but call my lawyer with updates, and wait. I didn't know what we were waiting for, but I was about to find out.

It was a Saturday night in August, and Eli came home earlier than usual. I was surprised when he greeted me—gruffly, but still, we hadn't been speaking at all.

"It's slow enough at the office," he said. "If you want to go to the club tomorrow, you can." I had a membership to a health club with a swimming pool, but I had not been there in months; since Eli had fired our housekeeper, there was no money for babysitters. I had been spending all day, every day, with my sons for many weeks. "I'll stay with the boys," he continued. "You can have four hours." He wasn't looking at me as he spoke, but I was so thrilled to have an afternoon to swim and exercise and try and release some of the stress I had been under that I didn't question this unexpected consideration. I thanked him awkwardly and went to bed.

The next morning Eli didn't go to the office, but spent the morning with the boys, watching cartoons and reading the papers while I prepared to go out. I was so looking forward to it: time away from this apartment, a break from the kids, a chance to exercise my stiff, underused muscles. Around one o'clock, I kissed the boys goodbye and left for the health club.

When I returned at the appointed hour, around five PM, I walked into the foyer of the apartment and put down my gym bag. Something felt different. The house was too quiet. The television wasn't on. I walked through the living room toward the dining room table, looking for a note. Nothing. I called out.

"Hello? Mitchell, Jared, I'm home."

No answer. Silence. I walked through the kitchen, toward the room my sons shared. The door was closed. The silence in the apartment was oppressing me. I should have heard Jared's high-pitched toddlerspeak. I should have heard Mitchell bossing him around. The TV should have been on, or music from the record player. There should have been a note telling me where my children were.

I walked across the hall and approached the boys' room slowly, my hand trembling as I reached for the knob. I pushed the door open and stepped into a completely empty room. Every piece of furniture, toy, article of clothing— gone. I was stunned and shocked. There wasn't anything at all in the room. I just couldn't believe my eyes. This could not be happening.

I called out for my sons as I stood frozen in the stripped room. "Mitchell! Jared! Where are you?"

I was in the room, screaming and crying,

"Mitchell! Jared! It's Mommy. Where are you?"

I ran around and around the apartment in a circle, from their bedroom into the hall through the living room into the dining area, through the kitchen and back into their bedroom, hysterically crying, repeating my desperate query as if they could answer.

"Mitchell! Jared! Where are you?"

Where was all their furniture and all their clothes? The closet door was open. The closet was completely empty. Eli, Mitchell, Jared and all their belongings were gone from our house. There wasn't even a note. Nothing. I sank immediately into profound despair. Oh, my God, I thought. Where are my children? Where did Eli take them? Are they all right? I was on the verge of hysteria. I backed out of the boys' room and walked slowly through the kitchen to the dining room, where I lowered myself carefully into a chair. I felt like I was one hundred years old. I needed help but there was no one, no one I could call. I put my head in my hands and let the tears flow. He took my children.

He took my boys.

Over the next few weeks, several things happened. I moved out of my apartment because I couldn't stop looking for my sons. I called movers, put most of our things in storage, and took a roommate situation on the Upper East Side. But after a few days, I couldn't stand being away from the place where Jared and Mitchell had been. I kept thinking it was a maneuver on Eli's part. I kept expecting them to come bursting through the door, telling me about the great adventure they had been on with Daddy, and I wanted to make sure I was there to greet them.

I had my dresser and belongings moved back home. I had my first breakdown.

I heard from Eli. He told me he had rented an apartment in Yonkers, and that the boys were better off with him.

I got an Eviction Notice. Turns out Eli had not been paying the rent.

I attended a hearing in Eli's office, during which I was presented with a Separation Agreement explaining our "shared" custody arrangement. My visitation rights were every other weekend plus every other holiday. I signed it.

I decided that I just wanted to die. I decided that if I got into bed and lay perfectly still, without moving a muscle, eventually God would take my life and I wouldn't have to confront all these problems I was incapable of solving. I thought that if I could just jump out the window, everything would be better.

I was exceedingly depressed. But I didn't try to physically hurt myself. No, I just got into bed. After a long, long while, it was very uncomfortable lying on one side. My arm hurt. I stayed in that position. But, finally, it hurt so much that I changed my position. I thought that meant I didn't really want to die.

So I found a psychiatrist.

My new psychiatrist, named Morris Jordan, had an office in the East Sixties. I saw him once a week and then I came home and got back into bed.

Eventually, I started to read some self-help books. Eventually, I started to care about living. With the support and help of Morris, I put an ad in *the New York Times* to find a housemate to share the rent.

Eventually Eli and I came to a financial agreement that provided me with alimony, as I had no source of income and not even the money with which I came into the marriage. Eli agreed to a complicated payment schedule which would decline gradually over time, beginning with almost nine hundred dollars a week (to enable me to catch up on bills he had neglected) with payments reduced over time until, finally, he would be obligated to pay me one hundred dollars a week, until I died or remarried.

I always knew he would never pay it.

Eventually I found a lawyer to force him to pay thousands of dollars in back alimony he had never provided to me. I had been through two other lawyers and a disastrous attempt to represent myself, but nothing, it seemed, or no one, could make Eli fulfill his obligation to me.

Until I met Glickman—a bulldog of a man; a lawyer as clever and determined as Eli. I knew that if anyone could get my ex-husband to pay what he owed me, to *keep his word*, it would be Glickman. "You're the one," I said, pointing at him as I sat across his wide and untidy desk.

Eventually, after months of legal maneuvering, Glickman got Eli to pay by negotiating the amount he owed, which was by then thousands of dollars, down by half. On the day I arrived at his office to receive the check, Glickman informed me that the amount—what a coincidence!— equaled almost exactly his fee. I didn't care. Like my first date with Eli, when he lied to me about his height, it was never about the numbers. It was about telling the truth. It was about keeping your word.

Eventually, with my Master's degree and bilingual abilities, I got a job with the Board of Education and discovered, to my complete surprise, that I loved teaching and was good at it. My days were busy with students and activities, but my nights were lonely.

I never got used to seeing my boys just every other weekend . . . and every other holiday.

I missed them every day.

CHAPTER TWELVE

What I learned at twenty-seven is even more true at sixty-five: there are no do-overs. The list of things we regret—bad choices, mistakes, carelessness and thoughtlessness—only gets longer, as does the life we've lived. I know there are people in the world who say they regret nothing, they wouldn't change a thing. I don't believe them.

But one thing that does change, between age twenty-seven and age sixty-five, is our sensitivity to the complexities of the things we regret. We start to realize that doing things over, were it even an option, would not necessarily be the best one. Because life truly is a domino chain: topple one, and all the rest fall in a certain pattern. Change one thing about that pattern, and lives are altered. We are interconnected, bound to each other and interdependent. To wish for another chance, the opportunity to do it better this time, is to ignore the ways that our mistakes shape lives, and not only our own.

When I am at my lowest—depressed, lonely, frightened, hopeless—I find it almost impossible to resist playing the do-over game, the *If. . .* game:

If I had told someone I was raped. . . .
If I hadn't married Eli. . . .
If I had worked even after I was married. . . .
If I hadn't given Moses up for adoption. . . . .
If I had fought Eli for custody of Mitchell and
Jared. . . .
If I hadn't waited thirty-five years to search for
Moses. . . .
If I had told Mitchell and Jared they had a brother
before I searched for him. . . .
If, if, if. . . .

But of course it's not so simple. It's easy to say I made a mistake marrying Eli Kramer, but not so easy to say I wish I hadn't. My marriage to Eli gave me my sons Mitchell and Jared, and I wouldn't want a life or a world without them in it, exactly as they are, my sons and Eli's.

And in a darker, more complicated way, my marriage to Eli is responsible also for Moses' place in the world. It was Eli's emotional detachment that created such emptiness which led me to accept Alex's dinner invitation, which led me to the second rape, which led to my son's conception.

So no, I do not wish I hadn't married Eli. As unhappy as that marriage was, that's not a do-over.

What if I could turn back time and choose not to have surrendered Moses to adoptive parents? Would I make that choice? My heart aches every time I think of all I missed with my second son: I never changed his diaper; I never walked him to his first day of school. I never watched him play a sport, or graduate from anything. I never wiped his tears or got to tell him how proud I was of him. I didn't see him marry.

But I did not abandon Moses. I need to remind myself of that all the time. I gave him over to a loving couple who could offer him everything I couldn't; a man and a woman who cherished him and raised him up healthy and strong and confident. And, by some miracle that I could never have orchestrated myself, this man and this woman were of my faith. Despite the fact that I was turned away by a Jewish adoption agency; despite the fact of my lie about Moses' biological father being Catholic, my son was raised in the faith of his ancestors. There is something about that fact which comforts me when I think about whether I would remake that choice if I could. Because as hard as it is for me to admit this, I believe that giving Moses up for adoption was the best choice for him.

Would I change the career—teaching—to which I have devoted my life? It was not my choice. I pursued it to please my father. But no, I wouldn't do that one over either. It turned out to be richly satisfying, and I was good at it, and it has provided me with a generous pension to see me comfortably through retirement, as well as the qualifications for continued employment as an adjunct professor at local colleges.

Would I change my decision, which was never really mine at all, but rather the manipulation of a psychiatrist and a lawyer, not to fight Eli for custody after he took the boys? That one is harder, and more painful to answer honestly. I know what I lost by not having my children with me every day. But if I could go back, would I do things differently? I had no survival skills. I had to learn them all from scratch. The world I came from had passed me untrained from father to husband. I had to learn to be a single woman. I don't know what would have happened had I suddenly found myself a single mother. There were times when I doubted that I would survive the pressure, the depression, and the never ending struggle to make ends meet. But I did. I came through it, but without my children. I never got to know if I could have done it with them, but I fear I would have crashed, and then what would we have done? Would we have ended up on welfare?

So I reserve judgment on that one. But I wish I had had a choice. I wish that Eli and I could have talked about what was best for the boys. If we had, perhaps they wouldn't have suffered so much from my unhappiness.

Of course there are some things it is easy to say I would change if I could, some choices it pains me every day to regret. I wish that I had prepared Mitchell and Jared in a mature and compassionate way for the revelation that they had a brother. I wish I had known to do that. I was dealing with one of the largest and most respected adoption agencies in the field, but they never advised me as to how I should broach the subject with my other children, how to tell them about the existence of their brother so it wasn't a total surprise attack. I know now that Moses was too eager. I made a terrible mistake not to stop him from making that telephone call at twelve forty-five a.m., and I have paid for it by the rupture in my relationships with my sons. Unfortunately, I listened to the Social Worker at the adoption agency who told me that "an adopted child *must* be in control"; she also told me to "just *let him lead.*" And so, in my state of trying to do the right thing; I simply did. So, to this day, as a result of my reunion with Moses, my eldest son Mitchell has not spoken to me.

What else is on my list of regrets? What else would I do differently if I could? I would have respected their choices more completely. When Mitchell fell in love with his wife, I would have celebrated his happiness with him. But I interfered. I felt he should get to know Naomi better, and they got married in less than one year. My advice was not needed. I would do everything differently if I could—I would welcome my daughter-in-law, without judgment, without a feeling of impending loss—because she deserves that from me, and because to do so would be to respect Mitchell. I have sometimes put my own needs ahead of my children's needs. I have asked Mitchell, from the time he was a little boy, to help to support me, to understand my pain, to help me.

It should have been the other way around, and the fact that I can't turn back time and do it over with my boys is, in some ways, my heaviest burden. I am haunted by the ways that I failed them, starting with losing them and continuing through years of smaller things—thoughtlessness and distractions: I spent some of my precious, every-other-week visiting time with Mitchell telling him how badly I felt about living without them, asking for his support and understanding, instead of supporting and understanding him. He was a little boy but he tried so hard to be strong for me.

I remember a time when Mitchell was maybe ten or eleven, and the boys were with me for the weekend. It was a warm day, and Mitchell was stretched out on my bed in front of the television. I was sitting at my dressing table reading and when I looked over at the boys, I saw that Mitchell had taken off his tee-shirt. I stared, fixated, at his thin back, his narrow boy shoulders, his smooth, hairless, tanned skin.

I don't think I am the only mother to have gazed, awestruck, at her own child. Every once in a while, the reminder that *I made that; that boy is my child* can be overwhelming. It is so amazing to have a child, amazing and oppressive too. The responsibility a parent has for the *life* contained within the fragile little bodies of our children is more important than anything else. And when we carry, as I did, the ever-present fear that we are not up to that responsibility—not prepared, not capable—it is to carry an exquisite and specific kind of dismay. I stared at my son's bare back, muscled yet fragile, and wondered how I could ever protect him.

"Mom?" he called over to me. "Could you tickle my back?" He had loved that feeling since he was a baby.

And I just couldn't. When I didn't answer, he twisted around to see why I was silent. I was shaking my head, and I finally answered.

"I can't right now," I said hoarsely. I wanted more than anything to be able to get up, cross the room, and lie down on the bed next to my son, tickling his back, making him giggle and squirm. So simple and so innocent, but I could not do it. My boys came in and out of my life like waves. Every other weekend, when I dropped them in Yonkers, or, when they were older, walked them to the bus stop near my apartment; every other weekend when I kissed them goodbye, it was like losing them all over again and it hurt. But I did not make it better or easier for them by creating a distance that would ease that hurt for me.

There are no easy answers, and the more I know, the less I know. But if I could do it again, I would tickle Mitchell's back. I would do it tomorrow, if only he'd let me.

❧

It has not been easy to admit the many ways I let my children down, nor should it be. I was a woman without the tools to make good choices.

Now I must live with the distance between myself and my three sons, a distance that feels like an icy ocean or a bog harboring monsters. How to get across, how to reach my boys and love them and start to reverse the damage inflicted on our bonds occupies my every waking hour.

I'd like to ask my boys to forgive me. I accept their right to design their lives in a way that makes sense to them, and if I am not included in that design, I will mourn the loss of a close relationship with them and then I will find a place to use the love I have inside me. There is such a need for love in this world. It is hard to love authentically, and selflessly but I take on the challenge. Just tell me how to love you, and I will comply.

And I will always be your mother.

Because there is no such thing as a "mother in name only." My mother was wrong about that. Because it takes only one glimpse, one touch, one second of holding her child against her breast, and a woman is a mother—irrevocably and inviolably a mother. It is not a label, or a title. It is alteration on the cellular level, on the spiritual level. There is no way to deny being a mother. Our choice is not one of assuming an identity, but of how we enact the identity we inherit when we have a child.

EPILOGUE
ROSH HASHANAH, 2021

Soon it will be Rosh Hashanah, the new year, one of the holiest days in the Jewish calendar. The anniversary of Creation, it is a rare opportunity to revise and regroup: to create a new life for ourselves. This ten-day period, marked by the blowing of the shofar, or ram's horn, is a time of introspection and repentance, culminating in Yom Kippur, when our fate for the coming year is sealed. And that's where I began this book, with Yom Kippur. I have come full circle.

I've been here near Laguna Beach, California, for two weeks at a condo where I can participate in any activity or club in this awesome senior community. I've cherished my experiences of taking free courses through Saddleback College with some of the most creative teachers I've ever had: classes in photography, art media, creative writing, foreign film—you name it, they offer it.

Today I'm lounging on my patio, against a wall of sliding-glass doors. From here, I can see Orange County Great Park in the city of Irvine. Gazing out at this spectacular view, with my back to this unit I was so lucky to find, I feel like the queen of all I survey. The park sparkles in the setting sun, splashing streaks of apricot, coral and amethyst across the sky. Lush trees dot the landscape against the backdrop of the silent mountain range, which is a steady and supportive anchor in the midst of so much exuberance. I have always found these summers in California deeply healing. I am happy here.

I received two phone calls today, one from one of my grandsons and one from my son Moses. They each ended their calls with three words: "I love you." It doesn't get any better than this.

I begin to whisper what I remember from the lyrics to that old Al Jolson song, "I'm Sitting on Top of the World," allowing my voice to slowly grow in volume, until it soars over the treetops. It's about the feeling of perfect happiness. No more blues. Just singing and rolling along.

When I finish, I allow my thoughts to drift. It's hard to believe that nearly twenty years have passed since I wrote this book. Why did it take so long to publish? I was unable to do much of anything before now because only within the last couple of months did I receive the long-awaited news that Eli passed away. Until then, I was terrified that somehow, even though I changed names and intimate details, my ex-husband, an attorney, would find a way to sue me for libel. A literary attorney advised me that even if he could identify himself by a freckle on his left forearm, Eli could sue; he could swindle me out of the precious new life that I have painstakingly cobbled together. I couldn't take that chance, despite all the chances I've taken up to now.

Forty years ago, I was a scared young woman, living alone in New York City with no real experience of earning a living. My brief history of secretarial jobs didn't give me enough experience to qualify for most good jobs. My

husband had just moved out behind my back, taking my
two sons, ages two and six, along with all their clothes and
the furniture. The only thing I had left was the eviction
notice in my trembling hands. I had no home or family to
help me, not even a friend. I was totally overwhelmed. I
felt completely devastated, emotionally stomped to death.
I had no idea what to do next, where to go, how to live.

And then I walked into the bathroom, looked into the
mirror and remembered a line from the ancient Persian
poet, Rumi: "Tear off your mask; your face is glorious."
Little by little, I started to pull myself together with the
help of weekly visits to a psychiatrist. But a psychiatrist
can only do so much. My newfound tenacity and strength
of character came from the lowest level of my core. After
having my heart broken so many times, I summoned the
strength that was always buried within. I took a Teacher's
license test without any college course preparation and
managed to pass it and get my name on the Waiting List to
get appointed. Finally, after several years, I got appointed
as a high school teacher in the South Bronx, which now
meant that I had a permanent job within the New York City
School System. This was the path to my future; my pension.
I can't overstate how huge this was for me. I knew that at
last I could now stand on my own two feet and take care
of myself.

To my shock, I discovered that I loved to teach. After
enjoying success after success in the classroom, I took on
work as an independent consultant for a bank, creating
and presenting original workshops to the secretarial staff. I
remained in my old apartment, advertising for roommates
to meet the rent. When the building went co-op, I used my
inheritance to buy it outright. At last, I was starting to feel
like a real part of the city.

When the school system transferred me to Manhattan, I felt joyous and free—and a bit bored. I decided to create my own singles organization. Each month, I produced an event in a different Manhattan hotel, restaurant or club with a live band for dancing. My motto was: "More Men Than Women," and month after month, I made that happen. It was a magical time because now, I was running the show. After my disastrous marriage, I reveled in being able to create love between a man and a woman. I also enjoyed wearing all the hats needed to produce the parties. I became a celebrity in the singles business, and I liked it.

Then, before I knew it, I had the required number of teaching years under my belt, and I was able to retire—to leave the windy and cold winters, with an excellent pension and health benefits. It was February. I went away to a health center in California, where the days are warm and the nights are cool; everyday is paradise. I spent three months volunteering part-time working in the organic garden and leading exercise classes. Astonishingly, although I had made the commitment to work there before reuniting with Moses, I found myself living just twenty minutes away from him. What a cosmic gift Fate had given me! I was ecstatic. It was a most wonderful Mother's Day.

Ten years passed. I began to spend beautiful sunny winters in Florida. My plan: Arrange for a real estate agent to pick me up at the airport, take me for a job interview at a college, and then show me a three-month rental at a senior community. I walked out of the college with two contracts in my hand, both courses in the university's College of Education. An hour or two later, I had three contracts, including a lease. I had created an entirely new lifestyle in a single day.

Florida was good for me. I joined a country club, was accepted onto a tennis team, and excelled in tournaments.

I tried to swim on a daily basis. I attended a different live show nearly every night. I purchased my first car and became a comfortable driver. I even fell in love. After a year or so, however, I broke off the relationship, realizing that he was not the right person for me. I was no longer willing to settle, and I was certainly unwilling to withstand any more heartbreak. I had already learned that I could survive—and thrive—without a man. Besides, I had married myself years back at an ashram when I gave up cigarettes, over three packs a day, and alcohol. That's where and when I learned how to accept and love myself unconditionally. And, to date, I have kept my sobriety.

Through it all, I have always been a teacher. I found a new home at the Florida chapter of the Retired Educators of America. I also taught in my community and at the local Jewish Community Center. I always feel vibrant and happy when I'm teaching, making new friends, or learning how to improve my health.

Just recently, I was a passenger in a horrific automobile accident. How did I survive? I truly believe that my Higher Power was watching over me. While recovering from the accident, I then had to withstand, along with the rest of the world, the desolation of the pandemic. Oh my, how to change my life for the better once again?

The answer was California. The answer was to be able, at my age, to travel alone from coast to coast, to transform my life from the desolation of Covid in Florida, to reestablish friendships, to take a deep breath, and to look out on this lush green vista with clear skies and puffy blue clouds, to meet the kindest people, to complete this book and know I will finally publish it this year, to finally free myself from the prejudice and old-fashioned rules and regulations of the fifties and sixties.

This story started with an incredibly fast and easy reunion. I found a son, an Ivy League graduate, a self-made, very successful businessman, with an awesome wife and children that seem to adore me. It's the way they look at me, listen to me, and make me feel like a VIP, a queen bee. Can it get any better? This is the inscription that Moses wrote on my recent birthday card:

Happy Birthday Mom!

We appreciate you <u>so</u> much and
hope you have a Blessed Birthday and
feel <u>ALL</u> the love you have in your life from us
and everyone that knows you.

Love, Your Son, Moses

The children even thank me for all their personal qualities, like looks and intelligence, saying that if it weren't for me, they wouldn't be as gifted as they are today. They say, "Thank you, Grandma!" I equally cherish the loving relationship I have with my other two grandsons and their mother, Jared's family. They also show and tell me that they love me. I inherited a daughter-in-law who substitutes for a real daughter with her good heart, generosity, kindness, and thoughtfulness.

Such exquisite happiness! I introduced Jared to Moses; they live not far from one another. My intention was to keep family close. They appreciate and love each other.

Sadly, my eldest son, Mitchell, has distanced himself from us since the night of the reunion, more than fifteen years ago. Although Moses and Mitchell did meet in person, it was not a match. This is our reality. Only time will tell how their relationship and that of their children will evolve.

After all these years, people ask me why I told Eli about Moses' conception rather than keep it a secret. All I can say is that I knew that my baby would be *much* better off in another home. Ours was without any love at all, totally dysfunctional and had been since our honeymoon. My father instilled in me the need to tell the truth and do the right thing, and that's what I decided to do.

Nowadays, new state laws are presenting extraordinary challenges to *Roe v. Wade*. While the constitutionality of such legislation is being determined, many women are yet again prevented from making decisions about their own bodies—resulting in abuses such as botched abortions and unwanted pregnancies. In the former case, women's bodies often suffer disastrous consequences. In the latter, more adoptions will undoubtedly occur, some of which will cause disastrous consequences in the lives not only of birth mothers, but also of adoptive parents, and saddest of all, of innocent children. Given my own story, I find it unbearable to watch it all play out.

Revealing this story to the world in its entirety is a catharsis for me. I have learned to better understand and accept in myself what has been diagnosed as a case of PTSD, post-traumatic stress disorder. I have felt such pure relief and pure freedom by just getting this poison out, this trauma. I want to share who I really am; not just the facade, the shell of a person. And, by extension, I hope that others can learn to reveal their secrets, disappointments and pain. They will then discover the insight and understanding and acceptance that I'm trying to express here. Acceptance and forgiveness are the keys to living a better and healthier life with peace of mind. Along these lines, I think of myself as "Open Heart." Only people who have had their hearts broken, over and over again, and can feel such pain and survive, do find out just how strong they really are. It's a form of emotional growth. Your heart is broken; now it's open.

As Maya Angelou wrote, "The courage to own your own story is the bravest thing a person can do. There is no greater agony than bearing an untold story inside you." I can't stress enough how important this is for us all to reclaim our own pasts. To accept the responsibility and the right to interpret our stories as we see fit.

And if, after reading my story, people don't accept me or can't love me unconditionally, I finally understand that this is their problem, not mine. Today, I do not feel at a loss. I accept whatever my Higher Power brings me. I have lived the longest time with a great deal of emotional pain and loss. But for today, it's okay. I have regained so much. Whatever else is in my future, I will take each day as a gift and be as grateful as possible. I am no longer a prisoner of my own past. I am not a victim. In the course of writing this book, I want you to know that I actually fell in love with myself.

∽

I wrote this book because I had no choice. It had to come out of me. It was like giving birth. I could not, and then would not, stop this natural flow of finding out the how and why of whom I am today. Although I had copies of it printed almost twenty years ago and gave them to close friends, I needed to publish, to put my truth into the Universe. I need to be loved, understood and accepted unconditionally. Even before publishing, I was already okay with myself. I accept and forgive all the hurt and pain and agony.

I also wanted to explain the truth and circumstances of Moses' conception, of how I suffered through a rape and pregnancy in total secrecy. I wanted to share the fear and agony of going to an Adoption Agency in the 1960s and being told that because they were a Jewish organization, it was illegal for them to accept a baby for adoption if it came from a married Jewish couple. So, I was shunted off to another Adoption Agency nearby, and they accepted my baby as long as I lied and signed a document asserting that the father was Catholic.

I was not told until after I gave birth that it was also illegal for me to see my baby. I almost had a heart attack. Although bound in what felt like a straitjacket with my arms clamped to two wooden boards, I started banging my arms against the wall, screaming, "I want to see my baby!" Several nurses told me to keep quiet, that I was disturbing other patients. But I decided that I would see my baby no matter what, and I continued screaming and banging on the wall with all my strength. After what seemed like hours, they finally did bring me my baby. I was able to cradle him, count his fingers and toes, and tell him that I knew he would be very successful in life, and that my love would follow him everywhere. I was heartbroken. If I'd had any kind of psychological support at that time, it could have been life-changing for me.

In addition, I wrote this book to give answers to myself and to light the way for other women. I needed to confirm that I have always strived to live and communicate my truth to the Universe, to be authentic, and to do the right thing. I was raped twice. And, not only was my body raped, but my soul was raped, too. I was a suffocated young woman of the fifties and sixties. I suffered intense emotional trauma when I was forced to give up my baby, my own flesh and blood. I was completely unprepared for the pain, lacking not only support, but also self-awareness. All I had on my side was the will to survive and educate myself.

For others, I hope that you will come to understand the extraordinary challenges within the adoption triangle—adoptive parents and birth mother—as well as for the child. How to begin to prepare for the pitfalls inherent in the adoption process, including the reunion? I know that if I had been better prepared for the reunion process, I would never have encountered the tragic outcome of allowing Moses to control and lead the way. That telephone call to Mitchell at nearly one a.m. would never have taken place. And, Mitchell would still be talking to me today.

Part of the answer relates to adoption agencies and public policy, including New York Cuomo's adoption law. For the first time since 1935, when the state sealed adoption records, adoptees can now obtain their original birth certificate when they turn eighteen and learn the identities of their birth parents.

The solution, I believe, is internal. If we feel ashamed of our pain and try to hide it, we are not facing reality. I can now stand up, be honest, look in the mirror, and know that my feelings, of pain and anything else, are a part of me. Know that we have all been traumatized, some more than others. But trauma is only a part of our lived experiences. Know that we must follow our hearts, wherever they take us. We must learn to trust and love ourselves, no matter how difficult that can be.

Two summers ago, I went to Big Sur, California, for a weekend of introspection. It was there that I rediscovered the word *compassion*. We need to put our arms around ourselves and have compassion for ourselves. And I do. Please believe me when I tell you that this is the only way forward for our children, our grandchildren and for ourselves. I know, because this is the story of my life.

By the way, that old song I was singing while looking out at my million-dollar view ends with a line about heading for a fall.

But I didn't sing that part, because it's not true. No more falling. I've learned how to fly.

ABOUT THE AUTHOR

Diana Kingsley is a writer based on both the East and West coasts. She is completely bilingual in both English and Spanish. In her retirement, she serves as an Instructor of Creative Writing, Foreign Films and Holistic Health, and she loves to travel, learn, and live on the cutting edge.

PUBLISHER'S NOTE

Thank you for the opportunity to serve you. If you would like to help share this book, here are some ways:

- **Reviews:** Write an online book review

- **Giving:** Gift this book to friends, family, and colleagues

- **Book Clubs:** Read it with a group of friends

- **Bulk Orders:** Email sales@citrinepublishing.com

- **Contact Information:** Call +1-828-585-7030 or email: info@citrinepublishing.com

We appreciate your book reviews, letters, and shares.